前言 Introduction

梁瓊白

◆一九五○年生，廣西容縣人。
◆中視「我愛早晨」、華視「早安今天」、
　漢聲電台「生活掃描」、中廣「松柏村」、
　「中午茶」烹飪主講。
◆中央日報、中華日報、聯合報、家庭月刊烹飪
　專欄作家。
◆著有《今天食譜菁華》兩冊、《藥饍食譜》、
　《怎麼做好菜》、《中菜精選》、《百菜100招》、
　《玉米食譜》、《快手飯盒輕鬆做》、
　《快手套餐》、《中國饕餮客》、
　《如何成為廚房高手》、《餐桌經濟學》、
　《無油煙新口味》、《家常粥》。

電鍋，幾乎是時下每個家庭必備的炊具之一了，不只是由於它的方便、耐用，符合了金錢上、時間上的經濟、實惠，更是潔淨、無油煙的最佳烹調方式，因此歷經了三十餘年的考驗，依然屹立不搖，甚至連造型都沒有改變，可見它在日常生活中的重要性了。

這其間，無論來自國外進口，抑或本地新科技的產品不知出現凡幾，似乎都敵不過國人對傳統電鍋的鍾愛，原因無它，因為沒有任何一種鍋的功能有它齊全、便利的。

電鍋除了煮飯，並且兼具蒸、煮、燒、燉來完成菜肴的烹調，個中技巧只在水分的掌握、時間的控制，及事前、事後的輔助動作即可達成，除了可以保持食物的水分，也在表現軟嫩度的口感上，發揮出萬無一失的控制，而烹調途中，靠著電源開關的把關，更不虞有燒焦、燒乾的敗筆出現，因此，以電鍋取代炒鍋為做菜的工具是很值得推廣，也是很實用的現代烹調術。

但是，電鍋固然有其直接完成的特色，無疑的，也有其部分功能不足的瑕疵，例如添加有調味料時的燒煮，在著色及湯汁的黏稠度上，電鍋便難免有未盡理想之處了，此時借助瓦斯爐於烹調前或烹調後的再加工處理，來達成理想的效果，便成為必然的也是最直接的輔助方法了。

即便如此，本書中所設計的各項食譜，也盡量做到簡便、快速的原則，避免增添掌廚者過多的繁瑣手續，以及冗長的時間投入，畢竟，好做、好吃和快速仍是我們需求的目標。

在造型上，三十年來幾乎一成不變的外

觀，雖然色澤在近幾年增加了一些創新的選擇，也仍有業者再提供新創意的空間，如果能再投入些唯美又兼顧功能的設計，相信電鍋將是所有炊具中的常勝軍了。

在材質上，近年受到醫學人員研究報告的影響，鋁製品有釋出危害人體健康因子的成分，而電鍋的內鍋即為此等材質時，為了安全著想，不僅業者應盡速變換外，消費者本身也應留意此一問題的存在，而予自行更換，多使用不銹鋼的內鍋來炊蒸食物，避免長期使用鋁製品可能造成的傷害。

每一種材料的質地各有不同，需要的時間長短也不同，甚至為了表現不同成品的特色，也需要靠一些技巧的配合，這些小地方的訣竅，我幾乎都在每道菜的重點提示欄中，盡可能的做好明確的交代，以期減少學習者試做時的失誤，讓所有以本書作為烹調指南的讀者，都能得心應手，輕鬆完成，讓消費者信任炊具的功能的同時，也對自己的技巧有所信心，這樣，用電鍋做菜便非難事，而是輕而易舉的樂事了。

The rice cooker is the most popular small kitchen appliance in every Chinese family. Not only is the rice cooker durable and easy to use, but also makes cooking convenient, time saving, clean and smoke free. Since the rice cooker was invented more than thirty years ago, there have been a lot of new designs on the market. But the original rice cooker is always the favorite for its unbeatable full-function.

In addition to cooking rice, the original rice cooker is good for steaming, braising, and simmering. Because of the moist-heat cooking process, rice cooker cooking is an excellent method in terms of flavor, texture, moistness, and nutrition. The basic techniques involve time control, proper amount of water, and some preparation and touch-ups. When cooking food with a rice cooker, you will never worry about burning food with the automatic turn-off feature. The rice cooker works well for many tasks, but it isn't perfect. For instance, it will not brown food or produce a thick liquid in braising. The remedy is to combine it with conventional cooking before or afterwards. In spite of this, cooking Chinese food in a rice cooker instead of a wok is a new and practical idea and is worth promoting.

All of the recipes and techniques this book offer are quick and easy. After all, quick, easy, and tasty foods are the goals we are pursuing. At the end of each recipe, there are remarks providing tips for better results and easy preparation. Everyone using this cookbook as a cooking guide will gain confidence in his/her rice cooker cooking ability and make foolproof mouth-watering meals easily.

目錄 Contents

雞鴨類 Poultry

肉類 Meats

蔬菜・豆腐類 Vegetables & Bean Curd

湯類 Soups

點心類 Pastries & Desserts

海鮮類 Seafood

* 較長段的草魚，一次用半片即可，如魚段較短時可全部使用，但仍需將魚片開。 * 在肉面劃刀口，可幫助魚易熟並入味快。

* 選購沙茶醬時，以含油量較少者爲佳，油太多表示放太久已產生沉澱，會影響香味。

* Score fish only if fillet is rather thick. * When selecting shacha BBQ sauce, choose the one with fewer oil. It will be fresher and tastier.

* 醬冬瓜味道極鹹，不可再加有鹹味之調味料。 * 爲保持色澤的清爽，不宜添加有色澤之醬油或蠔油調味。

* 鱈魚以魚身圓渾、外皮淺灰者，肉質較佳，而扁身、黑皮的鱈魚蒸好後則易化水。

* Preserved winter melon is very salty, don't add salt in this dish. * In order to have a lighter-colored dish, do not add soy sauce or oyster-flavored sauce.

* Any firm-fleshed fish with few bones may be used.

沙茶草魚段 Steamed Fish with Shacha BBQ Sauce

材料／

草魚中段1斤、葱2支、蒜4粒

❶料：酒1大匙、沙茶醬4大匙、醬油2大匙、糖½大匙

作法／

①草魚中段洗淨、片開，只用其中1片，用刀在肉面切十字刀口（圖❶），放在蒸盤內。

②大蒜拍碎，切細末，加入❶料調勻。

③將調味料澆在草魚段上（圖❷），放入電鍋，外鍋加水1杯，蒸至開關跳起時取出，撒下切碎的葱花即成。

INGREDIENTS/

2/3 pound fresh fish fillet, 2 stalks green onion, 4 cloves garlic

❶ 1 T. cooking wine, 4 T. shacha BBQ sauce, 2 T. soy sauce, 1/2 T. sugar

METHOD/

① Rinse fish, score diagonally (fig. ❶). Place on plate.

② Mince garlic, mix with ❶.

③ Pour over fish (fig. ❷). Place in rice cooker. Add 1 c. water in rice cooker, steam until switch turns off. Remove. Sprinkle with chopped green onion.

醬冬瓜蒸鱈魚 Steamed Fish with Preserved Winter Melon

材料／

鱈魚2片、葱1支、薑1小塊、醬冬瓜2兩

❶料：酒1大匙、糖1大匙、胡椒粉少許

作法／

①鱈魚洗淨，放盤內。

②醬冬瓜切碎，拌入❶料（圖❶）。

③將調勻的醬冬瓜及❶料澆在鱈魚上，並鋪下葱段及薑片（圖❷），放入電鍋，外鍋加水1杯，蒸至開關跳起時取出。

④揀除葱、薑，另換乾淨盤子裝盛即可。

INGREDIENTS/

2 fish steaks, 1 stalk green onion, 1 small piece ginger, 3 oz. preserved winter melon

❶ 1 T. cooking wine, 1 T. sugar, pinch white pepper

METHOD/

① Rinse fish, place on plate.

② Mince preserved winter melon, mix with ❶ (fig. ❶).

③ Pour over fish. Arrange sectioned green onion and sliced ginger on top (fig. ❷). Place in rice cooker. Add 1 c. water in rice cooker, steam until switch turns off. Remove.

④ Remove and discard green onion and ginger. Transfer fish to serving platter. Ready to serve.

* 這道魚不限鱸魚，只要是新鮮魚都可以，但新鮮度不夠的都不適合，以免蒸好後腥味重。
* 樹子有兩種，一種是燙熟後加鹽醃成餅狀的，味道較鹹，用時需另加調味料，較麻煩，效果亦差；另一種是罐頭品，可在任何雜貨店買到，味較甘甜，
  調味亦適中，比較方便，打開即可使用。
* 樹子罐頭內之湯汁可同時淋在魚身上同蒸，有滋潤湯汁的效果。

* Use whatever fish is fresh and locally available.
* Tree seeds, available in Oriental markets, are sold in cans.   * Reserve tree seeds juice, pour over fish before cooking if desired.

---

* 雪裏紅有兩種，色綠者較嫩，適合用於炒，色黑者較香，用於煮湯及蒸魚。
* 雪裏紅切碎後拌入豬油再蒸，除滋潤雪裏紅的口感，使之不致太乾澀外，亦有潤滑魚肉的效果，沒有豬油時，可用沙拉油代替。
* 天冷時，蒸好的魚要換盤時，要先將盤子用開水燙熱再換，避免盤子冰冷容易降低魚溫而影響口感，因為魚肉冷了會硬也會腥。

* Preserved mustard green is sold in cans, available in Oriental markets.
* You may use cooking oil instead of lard.
* Serve hot for the best taste. In winter, warm serving platter with hot water before transfering fish. Cold platter will lower fish temperature.

樹子蒸魚 Steamed Fish with Tree Seeds

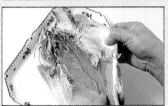

材料╱
鱸魚1條（約1斤）、樹子罐頭1罐、葱2支、薑2片
❶料：酒1大匙、鹽½茶匙、胡椒粉少許、豬油1大匙
作法╱
①鱸魚洗淨，由腹部剖開，成為背部相連之片狀（圖❶）。
②將❶料中之酒、鹽、胡椒粉抹在魚身，醃10分鐘。
③將魚放在蒸盤內，淋入豬油及樹子，並鋪上葱段、薑片（圖❷），放入電鍋，外鍋加水1杯，蒸至開關跳起時取出，揀除葱、薑，另用乾淨盤裝盛即可食用。

INGREDIENTS/
1 whole perch, 1 can tree seeds, 2 stalks green onion, 2 slices ginger
❶ 1 T. cooking wine, 1/2 t. salt, pinch white pepper, 1 T. lard
METHOD/
① Clean fish. Cut fish open from head to tail along stomach side (fig. ❶).
② Rub with ❶ except lard, let stand for 10 minutes.
③ Place on plate. Sprinkle with lard and tree seeds. Place sectioned green onion and sliced ginger on top (fig. ❷). Place in rice cooker. Add 1 c. water in rice cooker, steam until switch turns off. Remove from rice cooker. Remove and discard green onion and ginger. Transfer fish to serving platter.

雪菜蒸黃魚 Steamed Fish with Preserved Mustard Green

材料╱
黃魚1條（12兩至1斤）、雪裏紅4兩、葱2支、薑1小塊
❶料：酒1大匙、鹽1茶匙、胡椒粉少許
❷料：豬油2大匙
作法╱
①黃魚洗淨，撕除頭皮，並由魚背逆向由尾向頭撕除背鰭（圖❶）。
②魚剖開成1大片，加❶料抹勻醃10分鐘，放在蒸盤內。
③雪裏紅洗淨、切碎，擠乾水分，拌入❷料，鋪在魚身上，並放下葱段及薑片（圖❷），移入電鍋，外鍋加水1杯，蒸至開關跳起時取出，揀除葱、薑，換乾淨盤子裝盛即可。

INGREDIENTS/
1 whole fish, 6 oz. preserved mustard green, 2 stalks green onion, 1 small piece ginger
❶ 1 T. cooking wine, 1 t. salt, pinch white pepper
❷ 2 T. lard
METHOD/
① Clean fish, trim off fins (fig. ❶).
② Cut fish open from head to tail along stomach side. Rub with ❶ and let stand for 10 minutes. Place on plate.
③ Rinse preserved mustard green, chop finely. Squeeze out excess water, mix with ❷. Place on fish. Add sectioned green onion and sliced ginger (fig. ❷). Place in rice cooker. Add 1 c. water in rice cooker, steam until switch turns off. Remove from rice cooker. Remove and discard green onion and ginger. Transfer fish to serving platter.

* 海魚的魚頭肉層厚實，較適合蒸，故此菜以海魚頭爲主，淡水魚魚頭較小且刺多，紅燒較好吃，蒸的口感較差。
* 喜食辣者，可在調味料內添加辣豆瓣，但任何醬類均經發酵製作，故需用油爆炒過再淋下蒸會較好吃。

* Use firm-fleshed salt-water fish head such as salmon head for steaming. Bony fresh-water fish head is good for red-cooking.
* Add hot bean sauce to suit your own taste. Since it is fermented, you must stir-fry it with oil to bring out the flavor before adding to the fish.

* 石斑魚肉可在菜場魚攤買到已片除乾淨之魚肉，以色澤白、有光澤、有彈性之魚肉即爲新鮮度較高的魚肉。
* 家鄉肉味道鹹，要先煮一次以去除鹹味並可防止蒸熟後變形，而夾入魚片中則有調味及提鮮之功能。

* When selecting fresh fish fillets, choose fillets that are moist and firm.
* Virginia ham is rather salty. Cook in water to remove excess salt and prevent it from shrinking.

蒜茸魚頭 Garlic Fish Head

材料／
魚頭1個（馬加魚、加納魚、鮭魚均可）、葱2支、大蒜3粒
❶料：酒1大匙、蠔油3大匙、糖1大匙、鹽½茶匙、胡椒粉少許
作法／
①魚頭洗淨，切成粗大塊（圖❶），放蒸盤內。
②將大蒜拍碎、切細，與❶料調勻，淋在魚頭上，並鋪下葱段（圖
　❷），放入電鍋，外鍋加水2杯。
③蒸至開關跳起時取出，揀除葱段，即可食用。

INGREDIENTS/
1 fish head, 2 stalks green onion, 3 cloves garlic
❶ 1 T. cooking wine, 3 T. oyster-flavored sauce, 1 T. sugar, 1/2 t. salt,
   pinch white pepper
METHOD/
① Rinse fish head, cut into large pieces (fig. ❶). Place on plate.
② Mince garlic, mix with ❶. Pour over fish head. Add sectioned green onion
   (fig. ❷). Place in rice cooker. Add 2 c. water in rice cooker.
③ Steam until switch turns off. Remove from rice cooker. Remove and discard
   green onion. Serve immediately.

麒麟石斑 Chiling Sea Bass

材料／
海石斑魚肉10兩、香菇4朵、家鄉肉6兩、葱2支、薑1小塊
❶料：蛋白½個、鹽½茶匙、胡椒粉少許、太白粉½大匙
❷料：酒1大匙、豬油1大匙
❸料：太白粉水1大匙、清水½杯
作法／
①石斑魚肉洗淨，切成5公分長、1公分厚之長片，並加❶料拌勻，
　醃10分鐘（圖❶）。
②香菇泡軟，去蒂切長片，家鄉肉先煮熟，以去除鹹味，再去皮切
　與魚片同寬之片狀。
③醃好的魚片以1片魚肉、1片香菇、1片家鄉肉之排列狀，整齊排在
　抹過少許油之蒸盤內（圖❷），並淋入❷料。
④放入電鍋，外鍋加水1杯，蒸至開關跳起時取出，另將泌出之湯汁
　用炒鍋加❸料煮滾，淋在魚肉上即可。

INGREDIENTS/
3/4 pound sea bass fillet, 4 dried black mushrooms, 1/2 pound Virginia ham,
2 stalks green onion, 1 small piece ginger
❶ 1/2 egg white, 1/2 t. salt, pinch white pepper, 1/2 T. cornstarch
❷ 1 T. cooking wine, 1 T. lard
❸ 1 T. cornstarch solution, 1/2 c. water
METHOD/
① Rinse fish, cut into 5" x 1/2" slices. Marinate with ❶ for 10 minutes (fig. ❶).
② Soak dried black mushrooms to soften. Remove and discard stems. Slant
   into slices. Cook ham in water until done to remove salty taste. Trim off skin,
   cut into 5" x 1/2" slices.
③ Arrange fish, black mushroom and ham in pattern on oiled plate (fig. ❷).
   Drizzle ❷ on top.
④ Place in rice cooker. Add 1 c. water in rice cooker, steam until switch turns
   off. Remove. Carefully tip plate, pour off liquid into saucepan. Add ❸, bring
   to boil. Pour over fish and serve.

梅醬蒸蟹 Steamed Crabs with Plum Sauce

材料／
青蟹2隻、蔥2支、薑1小塊、薑蒜末1大匙

❶料：酒1大匙、梅子醬4大匙

作法／

① 用1支削尖的竹筷或竹籤，在青蟹兩眼間插入，先將活蟹殺死（圖❶）。

② 掀開蟹蓋，摘除兩側間之肺葉並洗淨（圖❷）。

③ 將蟹切小塊排入盤內，加入❶料及薑蒜末，並鋪上薑片（圖❸），放入電鍋，外鍋加水1½杯，蒸至開關跳起時取出。

④ 蔥切絲，另用炒鍋燒熱2大匙油，蔥絲鋪在蟹身上，淋下熱油，使蔥絲發出香味時即可食用。

INGREDIENTS/

2 blue crabs, 2 stalks green onion, 1 T. minced ginger and garlic, 1 small piece ginger

❶ 1 T. cooking wine, 4 T. plum sauce

METHOD/

① Insert chopstick or bamboo skewer between crab eyes to kill crabs (fig. ❶).

② Pull off broad back shell. Remove and discard gills (fig. ❷). Wash thoroughly.

③ Cut crabs into small pieces, arrange on plate. Add ❶, minced ginger and garlic, and sliced ginger (fig. ❸). Place in rice cooker. Add 1½ c. water in rice cooker, steam until switch turns off. Remove.

④ Shred green onion, sprinkle over crab. Heat 2 T. oil in wok. Pour over crab. Hot oil will bring out flavor of green onion. Serve immediately.

重點提示

* 活蟹未殺死前，不可將綑綁之繩索打開，以免掙脫後不易掌控而無法殺死。

* 蟹一定要新鮮才適合蒸，否則新鮮度不夠蒸好後很腥，殺後應立即下鍋，不可放置過久影響鮮度。

* 梅子醬可在雜貨店買到現成品，打開即可使用，買不到時，可用1兩話梅泡軟，將肉刮出剁細後，用油炒薑蒜末1大匙再加切碎的話梅肉，並加酒、糖、醬油調味後自製成梅子醬再使用。

REMARKS

* Purchase live or fresh-frozen crabs and cook immediately.
* Plum sauce is sold in cans or glass jars in Oriental markets. You may make your own plum sauce. Soak $1^1/_2$ oz. salted plums in water to soften. Remove pits. Mince well. Heat wok with oil, stir-fry 1 T. minced ginger and garlic. Stir in minced plum, add cooking wine, sugar and soy sauce to taste.

＊由於蒸魚的調味料及配料中的火腿均鹹，在蒸魚時極易被魚肉吸收而入味，所以魚洗淨即可，不必先醃。

＊這道魚的做法適用於任何鮮度夠的海魚或活魚，故沒有設限於一定的魚。

＊最後的蔥、薑絲切好後一定要泡水，除了去除辛辣味外，薑絲泡過水較白嫩，蔥絲則會翹起成不規則之絲狀，比不泡水更好看，有助外觀之美化。

＊ Since both cooking sauce and Virginia ham are salty, there is no need to marinate fish before cooking.

＊ Use perch, trout, or whatever fish is fresh and locally available.

＊ Soak shredded ginger to remove pungent flavor and prevent it from browning. Soaked shredded green onion has curved shape, which is good for garnishing.

＊小卷有的味淡，有的味鹹，洗淨後先嚐一下味道再決定調味料，本菜之❶料為蒸淡味小卷所用，若小卷本身鹹則不可再加蠔油。

＊薑絲切好後先泡水可保持白、嫩、脆，避免變色，並去除過重之辛辣味，能用嫩薑最好，若用老薑時要去皮並切愈薄愈細才好。

＊ Some salted baby squids are very salty. Taste before adding seasonings. If they are too salty, omit oyster-flavored sauce.

＊ Soak shredded ginger in water to prevent it from browning and remove excess spicy-hot flavor. If young ginger is not available, peel mature ginger with a paring knife. Shred as finely as possible.

三絲蒸魚 Steamed Fish with Three Shreds

材料╱
鮮魚1條（約1斤，鱸魚、銀花、鱒魚均可）、火腿2兩、香菇3朶、葱2支、薑2片
❶料：酒1大匙、蠔油2大匙、糖1大匙、胡椒粉少許、豬油1大匙
作法╱
①魚洗淨，拭乾水分，由腹部剖開成背部相連之片狀，並在魚身兩側斜割刀口（圖❶）。
②香菇泡軟，去蒂後切絲，火腿先蒸熟，去除鹹味後亦切絲，將兩者混合後鋪在魚片上，再將❶料拌勻，淋在魚身上（圖❷）。
③放入電鍋，外鍋加水1杯，蒸至開關跳起時取出。另將葱、薑切絲，放在清水中浸泡，以去除辛辣味，待魚蒸好後，撈出瀝乾水分，鋪在魚身上即成。

INGREDIENTS/
1 whole fish, 3 oz. Chinese ham or Virginia ham, 3 dried black mushrooms, 2 stalks green onion, 2 slices ginger
❶ 1 T. cooking wine, 2 T. oyster-flavored sauce, 1 T. sugar, pinch white pepper, 1 T. lard

METHOD/
① Rinse fish, pat dry. Cut fish open from head to tail along stomach side. Score fish with diagonal cuts (fig. ❶). Place on plate.
② Soak dried black mushrooms in water to soften. Remove and discard stems. Shred black mushrooms. Steam ham until done to remove salty taste. Shred ham. Mix shredded mushroom and shredded ham, place on fish. Mix ❶, pour over fish (fig. ❷).
③ Place in rice cooker. Add 1 c. water in rice cooker, steam until switch turns off. Remove from rice cooker. Shred green onion and ginger, soak in water to remove pungency. Drain, sprinkle over fish and serve.

薑絲小卷 Ginger Baby Squids

材料╱
小卷½斤、嫩薑1小塊
❶料：酒1大匙、蠔油1大匙、糖1大匙、魚露1大匙、胡椒粉少許
❷料：麻油½大匙
作法╱
①小卷洗淨外膜，並用刀在小卷上橫切刀口，嫩薑洗淨後切絲，用清水浸泡（圖❶）。
②將小卷放在蒸盤內，鋪上嫩薑絲（圖❷）。
③調勻❶料後淋在小卷上，移入電鍋，外鍋加水1杯，蒸至開關跳起時取出，淋上❷料即可。

INGREDIENTS/
3/4 pound salted baby squids, 1 small piece young ginger
❶ 1 T. cooking wine, 1 T. oyster-flavored sauce, 1 T. sugar, 1 T. fish sauce, pinch white pepper
❷ 1/2 T. sesame oil

METHOD/
① Rinse squids. Make crosswise cuts almost through. Shred ginger, soak in water (fig. ❶).
② Place squids on plate, sprinkle with shredded ginger (fig. ❷)
③ Mix ❶, pour over squids. Place in rice cooker. Add 1 c. water in rice cooker, steam until switch turns off. Remove from rice cooker. Drizzle ❷ over squids.

* 汆燙鰻魚時，可在熱水內加醋1大匙和鹽½大匙，如此可幫助去除外皮之黏液而不致使魚皮裂開，鮮味流失。
* 白果如用已處理過之罐頭品，則作法②可省略，直接打開即可使用。
* 河鰻要蒸久一點才會熟爛，若蒸不夠時肉質會發硬影響口感，而蒸好的湯汁帶有天然黏性，所以可以不必勾芡。

* When blanching eel, add 1 T. vinegar and 1/2 T. salt to scalding hot water. The purpose is to remove the sticky substance and keep the skin from cracking.
* If using canned cooked ginkgo nuts, skip step ②.
* Eel needs rather long cooking time. The texture will be tough if undercooked.

* 鱸魚有七星鱸和海鱸兩種，七星鱸肉細刺多、價格較貴，海鱸的刺較少，肉質稍粗，價格較便宜，但只要火候掌握得好，一樣可以蒸出不錯的風味，各有所長。
* 為避免最後一道淋油的手續不均勻，可在油燒熱後熄火，再將蔥、薑、辣椒絲放入，拌勻後再鋪在魚身上即可。
* Fresh-water perch has tender-firm flesh and is rather bony. Ocean perch has tender, flaky flesh. Both are good for steaming.
* In step ④, you may add shredded green onion, ginger and hot pepper to heated oil, stir well, then drizzle over fish.

蒸白果鰻 Steamed Eel with Ginkgo Nuts

材料／
河鰻1條（約1斤2兩）、白果2兩、葱2支、薑1小塊
❶料：酒1大匙、蠔油3大匙、糖1大匙、胡椒粉少許、鹽½茶匙

作法／
①河鰻放入8分熱之開水中氽燙過撈出，洗淨外皮之黏液。
②白果泡水1小時後，加水蓋過白果，放入電鍋，外鍋加水2杯，先將白果蒸軟取出備用。
③鰻魚切小段，放在盤內，淋上調勻之❶料，使其均勻吸收調味（圖❶）。

④將鰻魚放蒸碗內，倒下白果，鋪下切好的葱段及薑片（圖❷），放入電鍋，外鍋加水3杯，蒸至開關跳起時取出，揀除葱、薑，即可盛入盤內食用。

INGREDIENTS/
1 whole fresh water eel, 3 oz. dried ginkgo nuts, 2 stalks green onion, 1 small piece ginger
❶ 1 T. cooking wine, 3 T. oyster-flavored sauce, 1 T. sugar, pinch white pepper, 1/2 t. salt

METHOD/
① Blanch eel in scalding hot water (not boiling). Remove. Rinse well.
② Soak dried ginkgo nuts in water for 1 hour. Add water to cover. Place in rice cooker. Add 2 c. water in rice cooker. Steam until tender. Remove.
③ Cut eel into small sections, place on plate. Mix ❶, pour over eel (fig. ❶).
④ Place eel in medium bowl, add ginkgo nuts, sectioned green onion and sliced ginger (fig. ❷). Place in rice cooker. Add 3 c. water in rice cooker, steam until switch turns off. Remove from rice cooker. Remove and discard green onion and ginger. Place on serving platter and serve.

清蒸鱸魚 Clear-Steamed Perch

材料／
鱸魚1條、葱2支、薑1小塊、辣椒2支
❶料：酒1大匙、魚露2大匙、蠔油1大匙、糖½大匙、胡椒粉少許、豬油1大匙

作法／
①鱸魚洗淨，由腹部剖開成背部相連之片狀（圖❶），並切成兩段，鋪在蒸盤內。

②葱1支、薑2片、辣椒2支分別切絲並以清水浸泡，以去除辛辣味（圖❷）。
③鋪下另切之葱段、薑片在魚身上，並將❶料調勻，淋在魚上，放入電鍋，外鍋加水1杯，蒸至開關跳起時取出，揀除葱段及薑片。
④將葱絲、薑絲及辣椒絲撈出，瀝乾水分，鋪在蒸好之鱸魚上，另用炒鍋燒熱2大匙油，淋在魚身即成。

INGREDIENTS/
1 whole perch, 2 stalks green onion, 1 small piece ginger, 2 fresh chili pepper
❶ 1 T. cooking wine, 2 T. fish sauce, 1 T. oyster-flavored sauce, 1/2 T. sugar, pinch white pepper, 1 T. lard

METHOD/
① Rinse fish, pat dry. Cut fish open from head to tail along stomach side (fig. ❶). Cut into 2 pieces. Place on plate.
② Shred green onion, ginger and chili pepper separately. Soak in water to remove pungency (fig. ❷).
③ Place sectioned green onion and sliced ginger on fish. Mix ❶, pour over fish. Place in rice cooker. Add 1 c. water in rice cooker, steam until switch turns off. Remove from rice cooker. Remove and discard green onion and ginger.
④ Drain shredded green onion, ginger and chili pepper. Sprinkle over fish. Heat 2 T. oil, drizzle over fish.

Seafood

海鮮類

重點提示／REMARKS

* 魚露是由魚身提煉出的一種鮮味極高之調味品，適合用來蒸海鮮類，可在雜貨店買到。
* 魚露本身已有鹹味，故不宜多放，以免過鹹。 * 魚露打開後最好放冰箱冷藏保存，以免發霉、變質。
* Fish sauce is the extract made from fish. It is used for adding flavor to seafood. Sold in bottles in Oriental markets.
* Fish sauce is salty, do not add too much. * Refrigerate fish sauce after opening.

* 黃魚較長時才切成兩段來蒸，不長可以不切，而在切段時需在腹臍部位下刀較適合，若在中間直接切斷，在蒸熟後魚肉會外翻影響外觀。
* 扁尖筍有兩種，本菜所使用者為嫩尖扁尖筍，價格較貴，但不需切除硬梗，泡軟即可使用，另有一種較長的或捲曲成球狀者，有一段硬梗，需在泡軟後切除再用，以免過硬影響口味。
* 扁尖筍很鹹要泡水再用，以免過鹹，另外火腿的作用是提鮮，沒有的話可不加，或用家鄉肉代替。

* Cut fish in half only if it is too long. * Trim off any tough part of soaked bamboo shoot tips.
* Dried bamboo shoot tips are rather salty. Soak in water to remove excess salt. If Virginia ham is not available, just omit it.

蒸魚汁 Steamed Sea Bass

材料／
小型石斑魚2條、葱2支、薑1小塊
❶料：酒1大匙、魚露3大匙、糖1茶匙、胡椒粉少許、豬油1大匙
作法／
①石斑魚洗淨，瀝乾水分，放在抹過少許油之盤內（圖❶）。
②先在魚身上鋪下切好之葱段、薑片，再將調勻之❶料淋於魚身上（圖❷）。
③放入電鍋，外鍋加水1杯，蒸至開關跳起時取出，揀除葱、薑，另將1支葱切絲後泡水，待魚蒸好後，撈出葱絲瀝乾水分，鋪在魚身上即成。

INGREDIENTS/
2 small sea bass, 2 stalks green onion, 1 small piece ginger
❶ **1 T. cooking wine, 3 T. fish sauce, 1 t. sugar, pinch white pepper, 1 T. lard**
METHOD/
① Clean fish, pat dry. Place on lightly oiled plate (fig. ❶).
② Place sectioned green onion and sliced ginger on fish. Mix ❶, pour over (fig. ❷).
③ Place in rice cooker. Add 1 c. water in rice cooker, steam until switch turns off. Remove from rice cooker. Remove and discard green onion and ginger. Shred 1 stalk green onion, soak in water. Drain, sprinkle over fish and serve.

扁尖蒸黃魚 Steamed Fish with Dried Bamboo Shoot Tips

材料／
黃魚1條(約1斤左右)、扁尖筍½兩、火腿2兩、葱2支、薑1小塊
❶料：酒1大匙、鹽½大匙、胡椒粉少許
❷料：豬油2大匙
作法／
①黃魚洗淨，瀝乾水分，切成兩段，用❶料抹勻，醃10分鐘（圖❶）。
②扁尖筍洗淨，用清水浸泡20分鐘，使其柔軟，並去除過鹹之鹽分（圖❷），然後切絲。
③火腿先加水蒸熟，再取出放涼切絲，與扁尖筍絲混合後加❷料拌勻，鋪在黃魚上，放下切好的葱段及薑片於魚身上。
④移入電鍋，外鍋加水1杯，蒸至開關跳起時取出，揀除葱、薑即可食用。

INGREDIENTS/
1 whole fish, 3/4 oz. dried bamboo shoot tips, 3 oz. Chinese ham or Virginia ham, 2 stalks green onion, 1 small piece ginger
❶ **1 T. cooking wine, 1/2 T. salt, pinch white pepper**
❷ **2 T. lard**
METHOD/
① Clean fish, pat dry. Cut into 2 pieces. Rub with ❶, marinate for 10 minutes (fig. ❶).
② Rinse dried bamboo shoot tips, soak in water for 20 minutes to soften and to remove salty taste (fig. ❷). Cut into thin strips.
③ Steam ham until done. Cool. Cut into thin strips. Mix with shredded bamboo shoot tips and ❷, mix well. Place on fish. Add sectioned green onion and sliced ginger.
④ Place in rice cooker. Add 1 c. water in rice cooker, steam until switch turns off. Remove from rice cooker. Discard green onion and ginger. Ready to serve.

蛤蜊鑲肉 Stuffed Clams

材料/

蛤蜊½斤、絞肉4兩、蔥2支

❶料：酒1大匙、太白粉1茶
匙、胡椒粉少許、鹽½茶匙

作法/

①蛤蜊洗淨，放蒸盤內，移入
電鍋，外鍋加水½杯，蒸至
開關跳起時立刻取出，使蛤
蜊皆已張口（圖❶）。

②絞肉再剁碎，加入❶料及蔥
花調勻（圖❷）。

③將絞肉一一填滿張口的蛤
蜊，並抹勻（圖❸），放入電
鍋，外鍋加水1杯，蒸至開關
跳起時即可取出食用。

INGREDIENTS/

2/3 pound clams, 6 oz. ground
pork, 2 stalks green onion

❶ 1 T. cooking wine, 1 t.
cornstarch, pinch white pepper,
1/2 t. salt

METHOD/

① Clean clams,place on plate.
Place in rice cooker. Add 1/2 c.
water in rice cooker, steam until
switch turns off and clams open.
Remove (fig. ❶).

② Mince ground pork. Mix in ❶ and
chopped green onion, mix well
(fig. ❷).

③ Stuff clam shells with pork mixture
(fig. ❸). Place in rice cooker. Add
1 c. water in rice cooker, steam
until switch turns off. Remove and
serve.

重點提示／REMARKS

＊蛤蜊在鑲肉之前，要先撒少許乾粉在殼內，肉才黏得住，否則一蒸即脫落。
＊蒸好的蛤蜊鑲肉會泌出少許湯汁，可將它淋回肉面，但由於量不多，故不需勾芡。

＊ Dust clam shells with a little cornstarch. Otherwise, the stuffing will not stick well.
＊ Spoon clam juice over stuffings before serving.

＊海參塞肉餡前一定要先抹少許乾粉，以免肉餡蒸熟後脫落。

＊除刺參外亦可用烏參或光參，但作法①的去腥手續一定要處理乾淨，否則會有腥味，去腥時不用電鍋蒸可用水煮處理。

＊ Dust inside of sea cucumbers with a little cornstarch. Otherwise, the stuffing will not stick well.

＊ The purpose of step ① is to remove fishy odor. You can cook sea cucumbers in water instead of steaming.

＊蝦泥和肥絞肉拌勻後，最好用手抓起摔打幾下，或順方向多攪拌，可增加彈性，口感更好。　＊蝦仁以草蝦仁、蘆蝦仁或斑節蝦仁肉質較脆。

＊ Mix minced shrimp and fat ground pork by hand in one direction. Throw the mixture lightly against the inside of mixing bowl a few times. This method will give shrimp cakes a better texture.

八寶釀參 Stuffed Sea Cucumbers

材料／

刺參4條、筍1支、蝦米2大匙、絞肉6兩、干貝3粒、香菇3朵、蔥2支、薑2片

❶料：酒1大匙、醬油1大匙、鹽½茶匙、胡椒粉少許、太白粉水1大匙

❷料：高湯1杯、酒1大匙、蠔油2大匙、糖1大匙、鹽½茶匙、胡椒粉少許

❸料：太白粉水1大匙、麻油少許

作法／

①刺參洗淨內臟，放入電鍋內鍋，以清水蓋過，加入蔥1支、薑2片及1大匙酒，外鍋加水1杯，蒸至開關跳起時取出，撈出海參放涼。

②絞肉剁細，干貝泡軟、蒸熟、切碎，香菇、筍、蝦米分別切細末，混合後加❶料拌勻。

③每隻海參內側先抹少許乾太白粉，再塞入餡料抹勻（圖❶），裝在深盤內並加❷料後，放入電鍋，外鍋加水2杯，蒸至開關跳起時取出。

④先將海參取出切小段（圖❷），放盤內，另將泌出之湯汁倒入炒鍋，用❸料勾芡後，淋於海參上即成。

INGREDIENTS/

4 pre-conditioned sea cucumbers, 1 bamboo shoot, 2 T. dried shrimps, soaked, 1/2 pound ground pork, 3 dried scallops, 3 dried black mushrooms, soaked, 2 stalks green onion, 1 small piece ginger
❶ 1 T. cooking wine, 1 T. soy sauce, 1/2 t. salt, pinch white pepper, 1 T. cornstarch solution
❷ 1 c. soup stock, 1 T. cooking wine, 2 T. oyster-flavored sauce, 1 T. sugar, 1/2 t. salt, pinch white pepper
❸ 1 T. cornstarch solution, dash sesame oil

METHOD/

① Remove entrails from sea cucumbers, rinse well. Place in inner pan, cover with water, add 1 stalk green onion, 2 slices ginger and 1 T. cooking wine. Add 1 c. water in rice cooker, steam until switch turns off. Remove sea cucumbers, cool.

② Mince ground pork. Soak dried scallops to soften, steam in rice cooker until done. Mince scallops, bamboo shoot, dried shrimps and dried black mushrooms separately. Mix together with ground pork and ❶, mix well.

③ Coat inside of sea cucumbers with a bit of cornstarch (fig. ❶). Stuff filling mixture into each sea cucumber. Place in deep plate, add ❷. Place in rice cooker. Add 2 c. water in rice cooker, steam until switch turns off. Remove from rice cooker.

④ Remove sea cucumbers, cut into small sections (fig. ❷). Place on serving platter. Pour liquid into wok, thicken with ❸. Pour over sea cucumbers and serve.

清蒸蝦餅 Clear-Steamed Shrimp Cakes

材料／

蝦仁½斤、肥絞肉2兩、香菇2朵、香菜1棵

❶料：蛋白½個、鹽½茶匙、胡椒粉少許、太白粉1茶匙

❷料：清水1杯、鹽¼茶匙、太白粉水½大匙、麻油少許

作法／

①蝦仁洗淨，拭乾水分，用刀碾成泥，加入肥絞肉剁細，拌入❶料調勻。

②香菇泡軟切絲備用。

③將拌勻的蝦泥先擠出蝦丸再按扁後放入抹油的蒸盤內（圖❶），間隔排入香菇絲，移入電鍋，外鍋加水½杯，蒸至開關跳起時取出。

④蒸好的蝦餅先將泌出的湯汁倒入炒鍋，再加❷料勾芡後淋回蝦餅上，撒下香菜屑即成。

INGREDIENTS/

3/4 pound shelled shrimps, 3 oz. fat ground pork, 2 dried black mushrooms, 1 stalk Chinese parsley
❶ 1/2 egg white, 1/2 t. salt, pinch white pepper, 1 t. cornstarch
❷ 1 c. water, 1/4 t. salt, 1/2 T. cornstarch solution, dash sesame oil

METHOD/

① Rinse shrimps, pat dry, smash with cleaver . Add ground pork, mince to paste. Stir in ❶, mix well.

② Soak dried black mushrooms in water to soften. Cut into thin strips.

③ Grease plate with oil. Grab handful shrimp paste, squeeze out balls from top of fist. Flatten balls slightly with palms. Place on oiled plate (fig. ❶). Arrange black mushroom strips between each shrimp cakes. Place in rice cooker. Add 1/2 c. water in rice cooker, steam until switch turns off. Remove.

④ Carefully tip plate, pour off liquid into wok. Thicken with ❷. Pour over shrimp cakes. Sprinkle with chopped Chinese parsley and serve.

重點提示／REMARKS

* 豆豉以小包的乾豆豉較香，但不宜泡水太久，以免香味流失水中。
* 除鯧魚外，也可以用其他魚做相同烹調，豉椒的適用性極廣，任何魚幾乎都可使用。
* Fermented black beans are sold in plastic packages. Must be rinsed and drained before using. Soak too long will lose taste.
* Any firm-fleshed fish with few bones may be used.

* 魚片除了要新鮮外，最好順絲片，可防止魚肉碎裂。　　　* 蒸魚時，魚片在盤內不要重疊，以免受熱不平均，影響魚肉嫩度。
* 花椒粒是麻味的來源，如果不用油鍋爆香的方式處理的話，也可以用花椒粉代替。但不可在花椒油內直接加入調味料和蒜末，因為溫度太高會影響香
　味，熄火後盛出再拌會較好。
* Slice fish fillet along grain.
* Do not overlap sliced fish on plate, it will cause uneven doneness.
* Szechuan peppercorn has pungent flavor. In step ③, add seasonings after removing peppercorn oil from heat. If you wish, use Szechuan peppercorn powder and omit stir-frying peppercorn with oil.

豉椒鯧魚 Steamed Fish with Fermented Black Beans

材料／
鯧魚1條(約12兩)、豆豉1包（約10公克）、葱2支、薑2片、大蒜、
辣椒1支
❶料：酒1大匙、醬油3大匙、糖1大匙、胡椒粉少許、豬油1大匙

作法／
① 鯧魚洗淨，拭乾水分，在魚身斜割刀口（圖❶）。
② 豆豉洗淨，略泡水，稍軟時撈出瀝乾，與切碎的葱花、蒜末、辣
　 椒末及薑末混合，並加入❶料調勻後，淋在魚身上（圖❷）。
③ 放入電鍋，外鍋加水1杯，蒸至開關跳起時取出即可。

INGREDIENTS/
1 whole fish, 3 T. fermented black beans, 2 stalks green onion, 2 slices ginger, 3 cloves garlic, 1 fresh chili pepper
❶ 1T. cooking wine, 3 T. soy sauce, 1 T. sugar, pinch white pepper, 1 T. lard

METHOD/
① Rinse fish, pat dry. Score fish with diagonal cuts (fig. ❶). Place on plate.
② Rinse fermented black beans, soak in water to soften. Drain. Mince green onion, ginger, garlic and chili pepper. Mix with fermented black beans and ❶, pour over fish (fig. ❷).
③ Place in rice cooker. Add 1 c. water in rice cooker, steam until switch turns off. Remove and serve.

椒麻魚片 Hot and Spicy Fish

材料／
草魚中段1½斤、葱2支、薑2片、大蒜4粒、花椒粒½大匙
❶料：酒1大匙、鹽½茶匙、胡椒粉少許
❷料：醬油3大匙、糖½大匙、鹽½茶匙、醋½茶匙、紅油1大匙

作法／
① 草魚由背部片下魚肉，並將魚皮剔除（圖❶）。
② 斜刀切下魚肉成長形魚片（圖❷），拌入❶料。
③ 蒸盤內抹少許油，再將魚片鋪在上面，並加入葱段、薑片，放入
　 電鍋，外鍋加水½杯，蒸至開關跳起時取出，揀除葱、薑。
④ 炒鍋內加油1大匙，小火炒香花椒粒後撈除，餘油盛出，加入❷料
　 及切碎的蒜末、葱花拌勻，澆在蒸好的魚片上即成。

INGREDIENTS/
2 pounds fresh water fish, 2 stalks green onion, 2 slices ginger, 4 cloves garlic, 1/2 T. Szechuan peppercorns
❶ 1 T. cooking wine, 1/2 t. salt, pinch white pepper
❷ 3 T. soy sauce, 1/2 T. sugar, 1/2 t. salt, 1/2 t. vinegar, 1 T. chili pepper oil

METHOD/
① Fillet fish by cutting through flesh along backbone, remove and discard skin (fig. ❶).
② Slant fillets into slices (fig. ❷). Marinate with ❶.
③ Lightly oil plate. Arrange sliced fish on plate, add sectioned green onion and sliced ginger. Place in rice cooker. Add 1/2 c. water in rice cooker, steam until switch turns off. Remove from rice cooker. Remove and discard green onion and ginger.
④ Heat wok with 1 T. oil, stir-fry peppercorns over low heat until fragrant. Remove and discard peppercorns. Pour oil into bowl. Add ❷, minced garlic and minced green onion, mix well. Pour over fish and serve.

Seafood

海鮮類

＊除明蝦外，亦可用草蝦或斑節蝦，但各種蝦之體積大小有別，故切法亦不同，明蝦切段，草蝦由背部片開，斑節蝦小，剪淨鬚足即可，不需再切小。

＊明蝦肉結實，故不宜久蒸，開關一跳起就要立刻取出，不宜爛，以免肉質變老。

* If you wish, substitute shrimps for prawns. Just cut halfway through along back with cleaver, do not cut into sections.

* Do not overcook prawns. Remove prawns from rice cooker as soon as switch turns off.

＊為避免蛤蜊久蒸使肉質變老，故開關一跳起即需取出。

＊拌勻調味料後，放置片刻再食用較入味。　＊冰涼後味道更佳、更入味，是一道風味不錯的涼拌菜。

* Do not overcook clams. Remove from rice cooker as soon as switch turns off.

* In step ③, let clams stand in sauce for a while before serving.　* Taste better if serving cold.

蒜茸明蝦 Prawns with Minced Garlic

材料／
明蝦4隻、大蒜4粒、香菜2棵
❶料：酒1大匙、蠔油2大匙、糖½大匙、鹽½茶匙、胡椒粉少許、麻油1大匙

作法／
①明蝦洗淨，用剪刀剪淨鬚足（圖❶），挑淨泥腸。
②明蝦切小段，並由背部以刀片開刀口（圖❷），放入蒸盤內。
③大蒜拍碎、切細，加入❶料調勻，淋在明蝦段上，放入電鍋，外鍋加水1杯，蒸至開關跳起時取出。
④另用乾淨盤裝盛，並撒下切碎之香菜末即成。

INGREDIENTS/
4 prawns, 4 cloves garlic, 2 stalks Chinese parsley
❶ 1 T. cooking wine, 2 T. oyster-flavored sauce, 1/2 T. sugar, 1/2 t. salt, pinch white pepper, 1 T. sesame oil

METHOD/
① Rinse prawns. Snip off legs (fig. ❶). Devein.
② Cut into sections. Cut halfway through along back with cleaver (fig. ❷) Place on plate.
③ Mince garlic, add ❶. Mix well. Pour over prawns. Place in rice cooker. Add 1 c. water in rice cooker, steam until switch turns off. Remove.
④ Transfer prawns to serving platter. Sprinkle with chopped parsley and serve.

五味蛤蜊 Five-Flavored Clams

材料／
蛤蜊1斤、蔥1支、薑2片、大蒜4粒、辣椒1支、香菜2棵
❶料：蠔油2大匙、醬油1大匙、番茄醬3大匙、糖3大匙、醋1大匙、鹽½茶匙、麻油1大匙

作法／
①蛤蜊吐淨沙後洗淨，放入電鍋內，外鍋加水½杯，蒸至蛤蜊微張口時取出（圖❶）。
②蔥、薑、蒜、辣椒、香菜分別切碎，放入蛤蜊中。
③加入所有調味料❶，與蛤蜊在大碗內拌勻（圖❷），再放入盤內即可食用。

INGREDIENTS/
1⅓ pounds clams, 1 stalk green onion, 2 slices ginger, 4 cloves garlic, 1 fresh chili pepper, 2 stalks Chinese parsley
❶ 2 T. oyster-flavored sauce, 1 T. soy sauce, 3 T. ketchup, 3 T. sugar, 1 T. vinegar, 1/2 t. salt, 1 T. sesame oil

METHOD/
① Soak clams in water to spew out sand. Place in inner pan. Add 1/2 c. water in rice cooker. Steam until clams open (fig. ❶). Remove.
② Mince green onion, ginger, garlic, chili pepper and parsley. Add to clams.
③ Stir in ❶ (fig. ❷). Transfer to serving platter and serve.

鱈魚拌豆腐 Cod with Bean Curd

材料／

鱈魚2片、盒裝豆腐1盒、蔥2
支、芹菜1棵、大蒜3粒、薑3片、
花椒粒1大匙
❶料：酒1大匙、鹽1茶匙、胡
　　椒粉少許
❷料：醬油4大匙、糖1大匙、
　　醋½大匙、黑胡椒少許、麻
　　油1茶匙

作法／

①鱈魚洗淨，放盤內，抹上❶
　料，鋪上切好之蔥段、薑片
　（圖❶），放入電鍋，外鍋加
　水1杯，蒸至開關跳起時取
　出。
②將蒸魚時泌出之湯汁倒除，
　鱈魚放涼，剔除魚皮，用筷
　子將鱈魚肉挾出成塊狀，放
　盤內（圖❷），另將盒裝豆腐
　切與魚肉相同大小之四方塊
　同放盤內。
③芹菜、蔥1支切碎，大蒜拍碎
　切細，混合，炒鍋內加2大匙
　油炒香花椒粒後撈除，加入
　❷料炒勻，熄火後倒入芹菜
　末、蔥花、蒜末拌勻，盛出
　淋在鱈魚豆腐上即成。

INGREDIENTS/

2 fresh cod steaks, 1 package
bean curd, 2 stalks green onion, 1
stalk Chinese celery, 3 cloves
garlic, 3 slices ginger, 1 T.
Szechuan peppercorns
❶ 1 T. cooking wine, 1 t. salt,
　pinch white pepper
❷ 4 T. soy sauce, 1 T. sugar,1/2
　T. vinegar, pinch black pepper,
　1 t. sesame oil

METHOD/

① Rinse fish, place on plate. Rub
　with ❶. Sprinkle with sectioned
　green onion and sliced ginger
　(fig. ❶). Place in rice cooker.
　Add 1 c. water in rice cooker,
　steam until switch turns off.
　Remove.
② Carefully tip plate, pour off
　liquid. Cool. Remove and
　discard skin. Divide fish into
　cubes, place on serving platter

重點提示

＊鱈魚蒸好要放涼才可以分小塊，否則容易碎散不成形。
＊盒裝豆腐不需加熱，洗淨即可使用，若用板豆腐時最好用鹽開水氽燙過再用，可
　去除豆腐的豆汁味並避免出水影響調味。
＊調味料炒勻後要熄火才可將切碎的辛香料放入拌勻，否則繼續加熱會使辛香料過
　熟而影響香味，喜食辣者可加辣椒末。

(fig. ❷). Cut bean curd into cubes, place on plate .
③ Mince Chinese celery, green onion and garlic. Mix. Heat 2 T oil in wok, add peppercorn, cook until fragrant. Remove and discard peppercorn. Add ❷, mix well. Remove from heat. Stir in minced celery, green onion and garlic. Pour over fish and bean curd. Ready to serve.

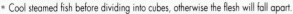

REMARKS

* Cool steamed fish before dividing into cubes, otherwise the flesh will fall apart.
* Packaged bean curd is ready to use. Blanch old-fashioned bean curd in salted boiling water before using.
* In step ③, add seasonings after removing sauce from heat. Add minced fresh chili pepper if you prefer a hot dish.

雞鴨類　Poultry

* 喜食辣者，可在起鍋後撒下切碎之辣椒屑。
* 醃鳳梨可在雜貨店或醬菜攤子買到，由於切碎後水分多，為避免電鍋蒸時滴水，故將雞肉用保鮮膜包好再蒸，即可保持肉面乾爽。
* 醃鳳梨酸鹹味重，故除了放糖之外，不宜再加鹽，而為保色澤清爽，不可加醬油以免變黑不好看。

* Sprinkle with chopped fresh chili pepper before serving, if desired.
* Preserved pineapple is available in Oriental markets. The purpose of covering chicken with plastic wrap is to avoid dripping from rice cooker cover during steaming.
* Preserved pineapple is very salty, don't add salt. Do not add soy sauce to this lighter-colored dish.

---

* 雞塊拌一層乾太白粉再蒸，除了避免湯汁流出外，並能保持肉質滑嫩。　* 雞腿要盡量剁小塊，蒸時才快熟也易入味。
* 豆豉以小包的湖南豆豉較香，洗淨即可切碎，不可泡水太久，以免香味流失。

* Chop chicken legs as small as possible for quick doneness and best taste.
* Coat chicken with cornstarch in order to preserve tenderness.
* Fermented black beans are sold in plastic packages. Must be rinsed and drained before using. Soak too long may lose taste.

醃鳳梨蒸雞 Preserved Pineapple Chicken

材料／
雞腿2隻、醃鳳梨8小片
❶料：太白粉1大匙
❷料：酒1大匙、糖1大匙
作法／
①雞腿洗淨，剁小塊，先拌❶料，使雞肉裹上一層乾太白粉後，放在蒸盤內。

②醃鳳梨切碎，拌入❷料調勻（圖❶）。
③將調勻之鳳梨淋在雞肉上（圖❷），蓋上保鮮膜，放入電鍋，外鍋加水1杯，蒸至開關跳起時取出，再拌勻後盛入乾淨盤內即可食用。

INGREDIENTS/
2 chicken legs, 8 slices preserved pineapple
❶ 1 T. cornstarch
❷ 1 T. cooking wine, 1 T. sugar
METHOD/
① Rinse chicken legs, chop into small pieces. Dry-coat chicken with ❶. Place in plate.
② Finely chop preserved pineapple. Mix with ❷ (fig. ❶).
③ Sprinkle over chicken (fig. ❷), cover with plastic wrap. Add 1 c. water in rice cooker. Place plate in rice cooker. Steam until switch turns off. Remove from rice cooker. Stir well, place on serving platter and serve.

豉汁雞球 Black Bean Chicken

材料／
雞腿2隻、蔥2支、大蒜4粒、豆豉1小包（約10公克）
❶料：酒1大匙、太白粉1大匙
❷料：酒1大匙、醬油1大匙、鹽½茶匙、糖1茶匙、胡椒粉少許
作法／
①雞腿洗淨，剁小塊，並拌入❶料調勻（圖❶）。
②蔥、蒜切碎，豆豉洗淨、切碎。

③用2大匙油將蒜末及豆豉炒香，並加❷料調味後炒勻盛出，淋在雞塊上（圖❷），放入電鍋，外鍋加水1杯，蒸至開關跳起時即盛出，撒下蔥花即成。

INGREDIENTS/
2 chicken legs, 2 stalks green onion, 4 cloves garlic, 3 T. fermented black beans
❶ 1 T. cooking wine, 1 T. cornstarch
❷ 1 T. cooking wine, 1 T. soy sauce, 1/2 t. salt, 1 t. sugar, pinch white pepper
METHOD/
① Rinse chicken legs, chop into small pieces. Marinate chicken with ❶ (fig. ❶).
② Finely mince green onion and garlic. Rinse black beans, mince.
③ Heat wok over high heat with 2 T. oil. Add garlic and black bean, stir-fry until fragrant. Add ❷ mix well. Pour over chicken (fig. ❷). Add 1 c. water in rice cooker. Place chicken in rice cooker. Steam until switch turns off. Remove from rice cooker. Sprinkle with chopped green onion and serve.

重點提示／REMARKS

* 買鴨肉時，用手按鴨胸脯，結實者肉層厚，有彈性，較好吃，若太軟則鴨肉腥。
* 鴨剁小塊後，先汆燙過以去除血水再蒸，可避免腥味留存，並避免湯汁混濁。
* 芋艿即小芋頭，可在菜場買到已去皮者，若買帶皮芋頭，則需先泡溫水，再用湯匙刮除外皮，不可用刨刀削，以免芋艿肉層被削除。
* 除芋艿外，亦可用大芋頭，蒸時讓湯汁淋在肉面，芋艿本身不調味，蒸好扣出時，讓湯汁被芋艿吸收即可達到調味功能，否則芋艿先調味不易蒸得鬆軟。
* When selecting duck, press duck breast to make sure it is firm and not soggy.   * Blanch duck pieces in boiling water to remove scum and odor.
* Baby taro roots can be found in some supermarkets and most Oriental markets. Soak baby taro roots in warm water, pare with spoon.
* You may substitute taro roots if you wish. Cook taro roots without seasoning to have tenderer texture.

* 用全雞、半雞或雞腿做醉雞均可，但以雞腿較富彈性，肉質口感佳，且人口少之小家庭，雞腿之分量較適中。
* 做醉雞的酒只能用紅露酒或紹興酒，其他酒精含量高者不宜，味道過重或過輕皆不適合。
* 雞湯一定要放涼，才可與酒混合，否則熱雞湯容易在浸泡後冷卻時結凍。
* You may substitute whole frying chicken, if you wish, although chicken legs are more tender.
* Only use Shaohsing Wine or Red Dew Wine. Wine with high percent proof or strong flavor is not suitable.   * Cool chicken broth completely before mixing with wine.

芋艿鴨 Taro Root Duck

材料／
鴨½隻（約1½斤）、芋艿1斤、薑2片
❶料：酒1大匙、醬油3大匙、鹽½茶匙、糖½大匙、蒜末1茶匙

作法／
①鴨洗淨，剁小塊（圖❶）。
②芋艿切小塊，鴨肉用開水汆燙過。
③將鴨肉鋪在蒸碗內，並將❶料調勻，淋在鴨肉上，再鋪切小塊的芋艿（圖❷）。
④放入電鍋，外鍋加水3杯，蒸至開關跳起時即可取出，用另一盤子扣出即成。

INGREDIENTS/
1/2 duck, 1¹/₃ pounds baby taro roots, pared, 2 slices ginger
❶ 1 T. cooking wine, 3 T. soy sauce, 1/2 t. salt, 1/2 T. sugar, 1 t. minced garlic

METHOD/
① Rinse chicken legs. Chop into small pieces (fig. ❶).
② Cut taro roots into small pieces. Blanch duck in boiling water, remove from water.
③ Place in deep bowl. Mix ❶ well, pour over duck, place taro roots on top (fig. ❷).
④ Add 3 c. water in rice cooker. Place bowl in rice cooker. Steam until switch turns off. Remove from rice cooker. Invert bowl on serving platter, remove bowl. Ready to serve.

醉雞 Drunken Chicken

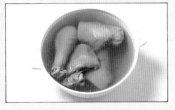

材料／
雞腿2隻、蔥2支、薑2片
❶料：紅露酒1瓶、鹽1茶匙

作法／
①雞腿洗淨，先汆燙過，再放入深碗內，加入切好的蔥段、薑片（圖❶），移入電鍋。
②碗內加水2杯，電鍋外鍋加水1杯，蒸至開關跳起時取出。
③將泌出2杯的雞湯，與❶料混合，再將雞腿切兩段，放入酒汁內浸泡4小時（圖❷），即可食用。

INGREDIENTS/
2 chicken legs, 2 stalks green onion, 2 slices ginger
❶ 2 c. chicken broth, 1 bottle Shaohsing wine, 1 t. salt

METHOD/
① Rinse chicken legs. Blanch in boiling water, remove. Place in deep bowl. Add sectioned green onion and sliced ginger (fig. ❶).
② Add 1 c. water in rice cooker. Add 2 c. water in bowl, place in rice cooker. Steam until switch turns off. Remove from rice cooker.
③ Drain, reserve 2 c.chicken broth. Mix reserved chicken broth, Shaohsing wine and salt. Cut each chicken leg into two sections. Soak in wine mixture for 4 hours (fig. ❷). Ready to serve.

文昌雞 Wenchang Chicken

材料╱
雞腿2隻、葱3支、薑1小塊、辣椒1支、大蒜3粒
❶料：酒1大匙、鹽½大匙
❷料：醬油4大匙、糖1大匙、醋½大匙、鹽½茶匙、麻油1茶匙

作法╱
① 雞腿洗淨，抹上❶料（圖❶）。
② 鋪上切好之葱段、薑片（圖❷），放入電鍋，外鍋加水2杯，蒸至開關跳起時取出。
③ 稍涼時剁小塊排入盤內，另將葱、薑、蒜、辣椒切碎，加入❷料調勻，淋在雞身上即成。

INGREDIENTS/
2 chicken legs, 3 stalks green onion, 1 small piece ginger, 1 fresh chili pepper, 3 cloves garlic
❶ 1 T. cooking wine, 1/2 T. salt
❷ 4 T. soy sauce, 1 T. sugar, 1/2 T. vinegar, 1/2 t. salt, 1 t. sesame oil

METHOD/
① Rinse chicken legs. Place in inner pan. Sprinkle with ❶ (fig. ❶).
② Add sectioned green onion and sliced ginger (fig. ❷). Place in rice cooker. Add 2 c. water in rice cooker. Steam until switch turns off. Remove.
③ Cool chicken slightly. Chop into small pieces, arrange on serving platter. Finely chop green onion, ginger, garlic and chili pepper. Mix with ❷, mix well. Pour over chicken and serve.

重點提示

* 喜歡雞肉口感更熟透者，可在電鍋開關跳起後，再燜10分鐘才取出，肉質較結實。
* 蒸好的雞腿用冷開水沖涼，可使外皮較脆，爲避免冷水不衛生，亦可用冷雞湯代替。
* 調味料❷除了用拌勻方式外，亦可用炒鍋以少許油炒勻再淋入，炒過就不需摻麻油，直接拌就好，以增加油潤感。

REMARKS

* If you wish to have tougher texture, let chicken stand in rice cooker 10 minutes more after switch turns off.
* Rinse cooked chicken with cold water or cold chicken broth in order to have firm and tender chicken skin.
* If you wish, you may stir-fry ❷ with some cooking oil instead of mixing. Omit sesame oil.

* 雞胸肉中摻少許絞肉，可使口感較滑嫩，完全用雞胸肉會太乾澀。 * 亦可加荸薺少許，能增加脆感。
* 加入的雞湯溫度不可太高，以免將絞肉燙熟。 * 沒有竹節時可用小湯碗當容器，或用哈密瓜、香瓜代替竹節裝盛。
* Adding ground pork to minced chicken breast can make it taste tenderer. Solely use chicken breast will taste dry.
* If you wish, you may add some minced water chestnut to have a cruncher taste. * Cool chicken broth before adding to ground pork.
* You may use rice bowls, honeydew melons, or cantaloups instead of bamboo cups.

* 蒸雞腿時，為使著色均勻，中途最好將雞腿翻動一下，使其均勻浸到醬油，且有助於入味。
* 蒸好的雞一定要放涼再剁，可避免肉塊碎散。 * 這道菜涼食比熱食好，故隔頓不需回鍋加熱。
* Stir chicken once during steaming to give it even color and doneness.
* Cool chicken before chopping in order to hold shape. * Taste better when serving cold.

竹節雞盅 Minced Chicken in Bamboo Cups

材料／
雞胸肉1個（約½斤）、絞肉4兩、干貝2粒

❶料：酒1大匙、薑汁1茶匙、鹽1茶匙、胡椒粉少許、雞湯3杯

作法／
① 干貝泡軟，加水1杯、酒1大匙，先放入電鍋，外鍋加水1杯蒸軟取出。
② 雞胸去皮、骨，剁碎，絞肉、干貝亦分別剁碎備用（圖❶）。
③ 將雞胸、絞肉及干貝混合，加入❶料調勻（圖❷），再盛入竹節內，呈八分滿，再放入電鍋，外鍋加水1½杯，蒸至開關跳起時即可移出食用。

INGREDIENTS/
1 whole chicken breast, 6 oz. ground pork, 2 dried scallops
❶ 1 T. cooking wine, 1 t. ginger juice, 1 t. salt, pinch white pepper, 3 c. chicken broth

METHOD/
① Soften dried scallops in water, drain. Add 1 c. water in rice cooker. Add 1 c. water and 1 T. cooking wine to scallops, place in rice cooker. Steam until tender, remove from rice cooker.
② Remove and discard chicken bones and skin. Mince chicken. Mince ground pork and scallops separately (fig. ❶).
③ Mix chicken, pork and scallop. Stir in ❶, mix well (fig. ❷). Fill bamboo cups with mixture about 4/5 full. Place in rice cooker. Add 1½ c. water in rice cooker. Steam until switch turns off. Remove and serve.

醬油雞 Soy Sauce Chicken

材料／
雞腿2隻、薑1小塊

❶料：酒1大匙、醬油1杯、糖2大匙

作法／
① 雞腿洗淨，放入大碗內，加入❶料，並鋪上薑片（圖❶）。
② 放入電鍋，外鍋加水1½杯，蒸至開關跳起時取出放涼（圖❷）。
③ 將雞腿剁小塊，排入盤內，另將湯汁煮開，並用少許太白粉水勾芡後，淋在雞腿上即成。

INGREDIENTS/
2 chicken legs, 1 small piece ginger
❶ 1 T. cooking wine, 1 c. soy sauce, 2 T. sugar

METHOD/
① Rinse chicken legs. Place in medium bowl. Add ❶, place sliced ginger on top (fig. ❶).
② Add 1½ c. water in rice cooker. Place bowl in rice cooker. Steam until switch turns off. Remove. Cool (fig. ❷).
③ Chop chicken into small pieces, arrange on serving platter. Bring chicken broth to boil. Add a dash of cornstarch solution to chicken. Pour over chicken and ready to serve.

怪味雞 Strange Flavored Chicken

材料／
雞腿2隻、葱2支、薑2片
❶料：酒1大匙
❷料：芝麻醬3大匙、醬油3大匙、糖1大匙、醋1大匙、花椒粉¼茶匙、辣油1茶匙、葱薑蒜末½大匙

作法／
①雞腿洗淨，淋上❶料，加2支葱、2片薑（圖❶），放入電鍋，外鍋加水2杯，蒸至開關跳起時，再停10分鐘，然後將雞取出。
②待雞腿稍涼時，再剁小塊排入盤內（圖❷）。
③將❷料仔細調勻，淋在切好的雞塊上即成。

INGREDIENTS/
2 chicken legs, 2 stalks green onion, 2 slices ginger
❶ 1 T. cooking wine
❷ 3 T. sesame seed paste, 3 T. soy sauce, 1 T. sugar, 1 T. vinegar, 1/4 t. ground Szechuan peppercorns, 1 t. chili oil, 1/2 T. minced chopped green onion, ginger and garlic

METHOD/
① Rinse chicken legs. Place in inner pan. Sprinkle with ❶, add sectioned green onion and sliced ginger (fig. ❶). Place in rice cooker. Add 2 c. water in rice cooker. Steam until switch turns off. Let stand for 10 minutes before removing.
② Cool chicken slightly. Chop into small pieces (fig. ❷), arrange on serving platter.
③ Mix ❷ well. Pour over chicken and serve.

金華雞 Chicken with Ham

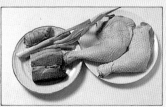

材料／
雞腿2隻、火腿6兩、葱2支、薑1小塊
❶料：酒1大匙、黃砂糖½杯
❷料：酒1大匙、鹽1茶匙
❸料：雞湯少許、清水½杯、太白粉水1大匙、味精少許

作法／
①火腿洗淨，先用開水汆燙過，再放入碗內，加❶料，移入電鍋，外鍋加水2杯，蒸至開關跳起時取出。
②雞腿洗淨，抹❷料，放入電鍋，鋪上切好之葱段、薑片在雞腿上，外鍋加水2杯，蒸至開關跳起時取出（圖❶）。
③雞腿、火腿都放涼後，再將雞腿去骨切厚片，火腿切薄片，每片雞腿中間夾入1片火腿，整齊排好在盤內（圖❷）。
④放入電鍋再蒸一次，外鍋加水½杯，蒸至開關跳起即取出。
⑤將泌出的湯汁倒入炒鍋，再加入❸料煮開，黏稠時淋在雞腿上即成。

INGREDIENTS/
2 chicken legs, 1/2 pound Chinese ham, 2 stalks green onion, 1 small piece ginger
❶ 1 T. cooking wine, 1/2 c. light brown sugar
❷ 1 T. cooking wine, 1 t. salt
❸ chicken broth, 1/2 c. water, 1 T. cornstarch solution, pinch MSG

METHOD/
① Rinse ham. Blanch in boiling water, drain. Place in medium bowl, add ❶. Place in rice cooker. Add 2 c. water in rice cooker. Steam until switch turns off. Remove.
② Rinse chicken legs, place in inner pan. Sprinkle with ❷, add sectioned green onion and sliced ginger on top. Place in rice cooker. Add 2 c. water in rice cooker. Steam until switch turns off. Remove (fig. ❶).
③ Cool chicken and ham. Remove and discard chicken bones, cut chicken into thick slices. Thinly slice ham, fill one slice ham in each chicken. Arrange on serving plate (fig. ❷).
④ Place in rice cooker. Add 1/2 c. water in rice cooker. Steam until switch turns off. Remove.
⑤ Carefully tip plate, pour off liquid into saucepan. Add ❸, bring to a boil. Cook until thickened. Pour over chicken and serve.

酸菜鴨 Pickled Mustard Duck

材料／

鴨½隻(約1½斤)、酸菜心3片、葱2支、薑1小塊
❶料：酒1大匙
❷料：鴨湯少許、清水1杯、鹽½茶匙

作法／

①鴨洗淨，先氽燙過，以去除血水，再放入深盤內（圖❶），鋪上切好之葱段、薑片，並加❶料，放入電鍋，外鍋加水3杯，蒸至開關跳起時取出。

②酸菜心修整齊後切成長片，放入清水中浸泡，以去除鹹味（圖❷）。

③待鴨身稍涼時，去骨取肉，切成長片，和酸菜心搭配，間隔排入蒸碗內（圖❸），加入❷料，放入電鍋，外鍋加水1杯，蒸至開關跳起時取出。

④先將湯汁泌出，再將酸菜鴨扣入盤內，湯汁淋回鴨面上即成。

INGREDIENTS/

1/2 duck, 3 leaves pickled mustard heart, 2 stalks green onion, 1 small piece ginger
❶ 1 T. cooking wine
❷ duck broth, 1 c. water, 1/2 t. salt

METHOD/

① Rinse duck. Blanch in boiling water to remove scum. Place on shallow plate (fig. ❶), arrange sectioned green onion and sliced ginger on top, sprinkle with ❶. Place in rice cooker. Add 3 c. water in rice cooker. Steam until switch turns off. Remove.

② Trim pickled mustard heart, cut into slices. Soak in water to remove salty taste (fig. ❷).

③ Cool duck till easy to handle. Remove and discard skin and bones. Cut into slices. Arrange sliced duck and sliced pickled mustard heart alternately in medium bowl (fig. ❸). Add ❷, place in rice cooker. Add 1 c. water in rice cooker. Steam until switch turns off. Remove.

④ Carefully tip bowl, pour off liquid, reserve liquid. Invert bowl on serving plate, remove bowl. Pour reserved liquid over and serve.

重點提示

＊選購半隻鴨時，最好挑選帶鴨胸骨那一半，可避免在蒸熟後，鴨胸肉乾縮，切片時不易整齊。

＊酸菜心很鹹，一定要泡水再用，最好先以鹽水泡10分鐘再改用清水泡，可使鹹味徹底去除而保持脆感。

＊最後蒸好扣出之酸菜鴨的湯汁，亦可勾芡後再淋，不勾芡較清爽，勾芡調味較濃。

REMARKS

* When selecting duck, press duck breast to make sure it is firm and not soggy.
* Pickled mustard hearts are rather salty, you must soak them in water before using. Soak them in salty water for 10 minutes, drain. Cover with fresh water. The salty taste will be removed and the texture will be crunchy.
* If you wish, you may thicken reserved liquid with a dush of cornstarch solution.

肉類　Meats

* 小排骨不可切太大塊，以免不易入味，即使蒸熟也會太硬。
* 小排骨以五花肉上方之子排爲佳，肉質較嫩。　* 蒸好後不妨上下拌勻，使調味料均勻再倒出更好。
* Ask your butcher to cut ribs into pieces.　* Baby back spareribs are recommended. The texture is tenderer.　* Stir cooked ribs to blend before serving.

* 絞肉以五花肉尾端較瘦之部位肉質較嫩，其次爲夾心肉。　* 冬菜極易含沙，洗時要等沉澱後再瀝出冬菜。
* If possible, ask your butcher to grind fresh pork shoulder for you.　* Rinse preserved vegetables well in case there is any dirt.

乳香排骨 Pork Ribs with Preserved Bean Curd

材料／
小排骨12兩、大蒜4粒
❶料：太白粉2大匙
❷料：酒1大匙、紅豆腐乳1大塊、糖1大匙

作法／
①小排骨洗淨，瀝乾水分，拌入❶料，鋪在蒸盤內（圖❶）。
②將大蒜切碎，與❷料拌勻作成綜合調味料。
③將綜合調味料淋在排骨上（圖❷），放入電鍋，外鍋加水1½杯，蒸至開關跳起時即可移出食用。

INGREDIENTS/
1 pound pork spareribs, cut into 1-1½" pieces, 4 cloves garlic
❶ 2 T. cornstarch
❷ 1 T. cooking wine, 1 large cube red preserved bean curd, 1 T. sugar

METHOD/
① Rinse ribs, drain. Stir in ❶, place on plate (fig. ❶).
② Mince garlic, mix with ❷.
③ Pour over ribs (fig. ❷). Place in rice cooker. Add 1½ c. water in rice cooker, steam until switch turns off. Remove and serve.

冬菜肉丸 Pork Balls with Preserved Vegetables

材料／
絞肉12兩、冬菜1杯、葱2支、薑2片
❶料：酒1大匙、鹽¼茶匙、太白粉½大匙

作法／
①絞肉剁細（圖❶），冬菜泡水洗淨後切碎。
②葱、薑拍碎，加水3大匙作成葱薑水。
③將冬菜放入絞肉中拌勻（圖❷），並加入❶料及葱薑水充分調勻。
④蒸盤先抹少許沙拉油，再將拌勻之絞肉擠成肉丸排在盤內，放入電鍋，外鍋加水1杯，蒸至開關跳起即可。

INGREDIENTS/
1 pound ground pork, 1 c. preserved vegetables, 2 stalks green onion, 2 slices ginger
❶ 1 T. cooking wine, 3 T. green onion and ginger water, 1/4 t. salt, 1/2 T. cornstarch

METHOD/
① Mince ground pork (fig. ❶). Soak preserved vegetables in water, rinse and drain. Chop finely.
② Smash green onion and ginger with cleaver. Add 3 T. water to make green onion and ginger water.
③ Stir preserved vegetables in ground pork (fig. ❷). Add ❶ mix well.
④ Grease plate with cooking oil. Grab handful pork mixture, squeeze out balls from top of fist. Place on oiled plate. Place in rice cooker. Add 1 c. water in rice cooker, steam until switch turns off. Remove and serve.

魚香牛腩 Fish-Flavored Beef

材料／

牛肋條肉1斤、葱2支、薑2片、
八角3粒、薑蒜末1大匙、葱花
1大匙

❶料：酒1大匙、開水15杯
❷料：酒1大匙、辣豆瓣2大
　匙、醬油1大匙、糖1大匙、
　醋½大匙、胡椒粉少許
❸料：太白粉水1大匙

作法／

① 牛肋條肉整塊先汆燙過（圖
　❶），再放入電鍋內鍋，加**❶**
　料及葱2支、薑2片、八角3
　粒，外鍋加水6杯，蒸至開關
　跳起時將牛腩撈出。
② 稍涼時將牛腩切片，排在蒸
　碗內，另用炒菜鍋放2大匙油
　炒香薑蒜末及調味料**❷**，並
　加入泌出的牛肉湯1杯燒開
　後，淋在蒸碗內之肉片上（圖
　❷）。
③ 將牛腩放入電鍋，外鍋加水
　3杯，蒸至開關跳起時，將湯
　汁先倒入鍋內，再將牛肉扣
　出盤中。
④ 將倒出的湯汁以調味料**❸**勾
　芡，黏稠時淋在牛腩上，再
　撒下葱花即可。

INGREDIENTS/

$1^1/_3$ pounds skirt steak, 2 stalks
green onion, 2 slices ginger, 3
star anise, 1 T. minced ginger
and garlic, 1 T. chopped green
onion

❶ 1 T. cooking wine, 15 c.
boiling water
❷ 1 T. cooking wine, 2 T. hot
bean paste, 1 T. soy sauce, 1
T. sugar, 1/2 T. vinegar,
pinch white pepper
❸ 1 T. cornstarch solution

METHOD/

① Blanch beef in boiling water,
drain (fig. **❶**). Place in inner
pan. Add **❶**, 2 stalks green
onion, 2 slices ginger and 3
star anise. Add 6 c. water in
rice cooker, steam until switch
turns off. Remove beef.
② Cool slightly. Cut into slices,
arrange in medium bowl. Heat

2 T. oil in wok. Stir-fry minced ginger and garlic and ❷ until fragrant. Add 1 c. beef broth, bring to boil. Pour over sliced beef (fig. ❷).

③ Place in rice cooker. Add 3 c. water in rice cooker, steam until switch turns off. Carefully tip bowl, pour off liquid into wok. Invert bowl on serving platter, remove bowl.

④ Thicken liquid with ❸. Drizzle over beef. Sprinkle with chopped green onion.

重點提示／REMARKS

* 也可以將牛腩先煮熟再切片排在碗內蒸。
* 牛腩煮熟再切片，肉質較嫩，且加熱後不易變形。
* 蒸牛腩時加開水，湯汁較清爽，避免血水再流出。

---

* In step ①, you may cook beef in water until done instead of steaming.
* Cook beef before slicing to prevent beef from shrinking. Besides, the texture will be tenderer.
* The purpose of adding hot broth to sliced beef in step ② is to avoid scum forming.

重點提示／REMARKS

* 絞肉可用五花肉或夾心肉。

* 只用蛋黃，不用蛋白，蒸好較好看，但可加少許蛋白拌肉當作調味代替鹽，但不可多加，以免太鹹。　　* 絞肉中可以加拍碎的荸薺，則口感較脆。

* Ask your butcher to grind fresh pork shoulder for you, if possible.
* If you wish, stir in some salty egg whites in ground pork, omit salt. Don't add too much, they are very salty.
* Add minced water chestnuts in ground pork to have a crunchy taste.

* 漂百頁時，最好等水開再放入，且時間不宜過久，以免爛掉。　　* 百頁放蒸盤內時，封口要朝下，以免蒸汽過高會掀開，影響成品外觀。
* Don't soak dried bean curd sheets in boiling water for too long. Otherwise, they will break into pieces.　　* In step ②, place rolls, seam side down, on plate.

鹹蛋蒸肉餅 Steamed Pork Patty with Salty Eggs

材料／
絞肉½斤、葱2支、薑2片、鹹蛋3粒
❶料：酒1大匙、太白粉1茶匙、胡椒粉少許、鹽½茶匙

作法／
①先將葱、薑拍碎，加水3大匙抓擠出葱薑汁。
②絞肉剁細（圖❶），拌入葱薑汁及❶料仔細調勻，鋪在抹過油之蒸盤內。
③鹹蛋取蛋黃，其中2粒拍扁後切丁，排在肉餅四週，中間放1粒（圖❷），做好後放入電鍋，外鍋加水1杯，或放在飯面與飯同蒸，待開關跳起即可。

INGREDIENTS/
2/3 pound ground pork, 2 stalks green onion, 2 slices ginger, 3 salty eggs, uncooked
❶ 1 T. cooking wine, 1 t. cornstarch, pinch white pepper, 1/2 t. salt

METHOD/
① Smash green onion and ginger with cleaver. Add 3 T. water to make green onion and ginger water.
② Mince ground pork (fig. ❶). Stir in green onion and ginger water and ❶. Mix well. Place on oiled plate.
③ Separate egg whites and yolks. Smash 2 yolks with cleaver, dice. Arrange around patty. Place remaining whole yolk in center (fig. ❷). Place in rice cooker. Add 1 c. water in rice cooker, steam until switch turns off. Remove and serve.

蒸百頁卷 Steamed Pork Rolls in Bean Curd Sheets

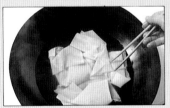

材料／
絞肉½斤、百頁1疊、葱2支、薑2片
❶料：小蘇打1茶匙
❷料：酒1大匙、鹽½茶匙、胡椒粉少許、太白粉1茶匙
❸料：蠔油2大匙、清水½杯、糖½大匙、太白粉水½大匙、麻油少許

作法／
①百頁放入開水中，加❶料漂洗至軟白時撈出（圖❶），沖涼、瀝乾備用。葱、薑拍碎，加水3大匙作成葱薑水。
②絞肉剁細，拌入❷料及葱薑水作成肉餡。
③每張百頁包入肉餡少許，捲成長條狀，排在蒸盤內（圖❷），放入電鍋，外鍋加水1½杯，蒸至開關跳起時取出。
④另用炒鍋將❸料炒勻，黏稠時淋在蒸好之百頁上即可。

INGREDIENTS/
2/3 pound ground pork, 10 dried bean curd sheets, 2 stalks green onion, 2 slices ginger
❶ 1 t. baking soda
❷ 1 T. cooking wine, 1/2 t. salt, pinch white pepper, 1 t. cornstarch
❸ 2 T. oyster-flavored sauce, 1/2 c. water, 1/2 T. sugar, 1/2 T. cornstarch solution, dash sesame oil

METHOD/
① Place dried bean curd sheets in boiling water, add ❶. Soak until white and soft (fig. ❶). Rinse under cold water. Drain. Smash green onion and ginger with cleaver, add 3 T. water to make green onion and ginger water.
② Mince ground pork, stir in ❷ and green onion and ginger water. Mix well.
③ Place pork mixture on bean curd sheet. Wrap tightly as spring roll. Place on plate (fig. ❷). Place in rice cooker. Add 1½ c. water in rice cooker, steam until switch turns off. Remove.
④ Heat wok, stir-fry ❸ until thickened. Drizzle over rolls and serve.

* 苦瓜先燙過再排入碗內，較服貼、易入味、快熟。　* 挑選苦瓜時，以顆粒粗大，色澤白的，苦味較輕。
* The purpose of blanching is for easy handling and quick doneness.　* When selecting bitter melon, choose the one with lighter color. It has a milder taste.

* 大腸頭肉層較厚，比較好吃，也可以用大腸，但以直腸較理想，做這道菜前要先將大腸用麵粉及沙拉油洗去黏液，再以酒及白醋揉搓以去除臭味，然後沖淨，煮爛再用。
* 鴨血買回來要泡水保存，以免因脫水而萎縮，汆燙過也可去除腥味。
* To clean intestine, rub intestine with flour and oil to remove sticky substance, rinse well. Add cooking wine and vinegar, rub well to remove odor, rinse well.
* Soak coagulated duck blood in water before using. The purpose of blanching is to remove odor.

涼瓜排骨 Ribs with Bitter Melon

材料／
苦瓜1條、小排骨½斤、大蒜4粒

❶料：酒1大匙、醬油2大匙、糖½大匙、鹽½茶匙、胡椒粉少許、太白粉½大匙

作法／
① 苦瓜剖開，去籽、切小塊，全部用開水先氽燙過（圖❶），然後撈出沖涼，先排在蒸碗內。
② 小排骨洗淨，加入❶料拌勻，先醃20分鐘，再鋪在蒸碗內之苦瓜上（圖❷），撒下切碎之蒜末。
③ 放入電鍋，外鍋加水2杯，蒸至開關跳起時取出，再扣入深盤內即成。

INGREDIENTS/
1 bitter melon, 2/3 pound spareribs, 4 cloves garlic

❶ 1 T. cooking wine, 2 T. soy sauce, 1/2 T. sugar, 1/2 t. salt, pinch white pepper, 1/2 T. cornstarch

METHOD/
① Halve bitter melon lengthwise. Remove and discard seeds, cut into small pieces. Blanch in boiling water (fig. ❶). Remove, rinse under cold water. Drain, place in medium bowl.
② Rinse ribs. Add ❶. Blend well. Marinate for 20 minutes. Place over bitter melon (fig. ❷). Sprinkle with minced garlic.
③ Place in rice cooker. Add 2 c.water in rice cooker, steam until switch turns off. Remove, invert on serving platter. Remove bowl. Ready to serve.

沙茶腸旺 Large Intestine in Shacha BBQ Sauce

材料／
大腸頭1條、鴨血1塊、蔥1支、蒜末1大匙

❶料：酒1大匙、沙茶醬3大匙、醬油1大匙、糖½大匙

作法／
① 大腸頭先洗淨、煮爛，然後斜刀切小段，鴨血切塊後先氽燙過，以去除血水、泡沫，然後沖淨（圖❶）。
② 將大腸與鴨血放在蒸盤內，加入蒜末及❶料拌勻（圖❷），移入電鍋，外鍋加水1杯，蒸至開關跳起時取出。
③ 撒下切碎的蔥花即成。

INGREDIENTS/
1 pig large intestine, 1 cake coagulated duck blood, 1 stalk green onion, 1 T. minced garlic

❶ 1 T. cooking wine, 3 T. shacha BBQ sauce, 1 T. soy sauce, 1/2 T. sugar

METHOD/
① Wash intestine. Cook in water until tender. Cut diagonally into small sections. Cut coagulated duck blood into pieces, blanch in boiling water. Drain, rinse well (fig. ❶).
② Place intestine and duck blood in medium bowl. Add minced garlic and ❶, blend well. Arrange on plate (fig. ❷). Place in rice cooker. Add 1 c. water, steam until switch turns off. Remove.
③ Sprinkle with chopped green onion and serve.

珍珠丸子 Pearl Balls

材料／

絞肉½斤、長糯米1杯、蝦米2
大匙、荸薺6粒、蔥2支、薑2片

❶料：酒1大匙、鹽1茶匙、胡
椒粉少許、太白粉1茶匙

作法／

①絞肉剁細，蝦米泡軟後切
　碎，荸薺拍碎（圖❶）。
②蔥、薑拍碎後加水½杯，抓
　擠出蔥薑水，連同❶料拌入
　絞肉中，順方向攪勻，再加
　入切碎之蝦米與荸薺。
③長糯米洗淨，泡水20分鐘後
　瀝乾水分。
④將蒸盤先抹少許沙拉油，再
　將絞肉擠成丸子（圖❷），裹
　一層糯米後放在蒸盤上（圖
　❸），移入電鍋，外鍋加水
　1½杯，蒸至開關跳起時即可
　取出食用。

INGREDIENTS/

2/3 pound ground pork, 1 c. long-
grain sweet rice, 2 T. dried
shrimps, 6 water chestnuts, 2
stalks green onion, 2 slices ginger
❶ 1 T. cooking wine, 1 t. salt,
pinch white pepper, 1 t.
cornstarch

METHOD/

① Mince ground pork. Soak dried
shrimps in water to soften. Mince
softened shrimps. Smash water
chestnuts with cleaver blade (fig.
❶).
② Smash green onion and ginger.
Add 1/2 c. water to make green
onion and ginger water. Add ❶
and green onion and ginger
water to ground pork. Mix well by
hand in one direction. Mix in
minced dried shrimps and water
chestnuts.
③ Rinse long-grain sweet rice. Soak
in water for 20 minutes, drain.
④ Grease plate with oil. Grab
handful mixture, squeeze out
balls from top of fist (fig. ❷). Roll
balls in rice to cover evenly (fig.
❸). Place on plate. Place in rice
cooker. Add 1½ c. water in rice
cooker, steam until switch turns
off. Remove and serve.

重點提示／REMARKS

* 糯米泡水後要充分瀝乾水分，肉丸才沾得上，沾好後再搓動一下使其固定，以免脫落。
* 丸子沾裹糯米時，要小心不要讓米粒陷入絞肉中，否則會夾生，蒸不熟。
* Drain sweet rice completely. Lightly roll balls so that rice sticks.
* Do not press rice into meat. It will cause uneven doneness.

* 五花肉的肉質較嫩，久蒸不柴，口感比夾心肉或腿肉好。先整塊蒸熟再切片，才不會因受熱而變形，也減少生肉蒸後出血水，影響湯汁的困擾。
* 蒸肉時肉皮朝下，上色較漂亮，帶肉皮蒸可以使肉皮的膠質流出，增加肉色的光澤。
* 五香粉比較輕，和其他調味料混合時容易浮起，需要慢慢調勻並溶化後再淋入肉內蒸。

* Precook pork before cutting into slices. The liquid from steaming will retain clear and the meat will not shrink.
* Arrange sliced pork skin side down for a better presentation.　* Mix ❶ and broth well before pouring over sliced pork in step ②.

* 紅腐乳不但色澤好看，且帶有腐乳香，並能使肉質軟化，但由於味鹹，故不宜多放，爲使湯汁達到上色及調味功能，所以加一些番茄醬均衡。
* 如用饅頭夾食時，應在饅頭冷硬時先切成活頁夾狀，然後蒸軟再吃，否則先蒸再切會因饅頭過軟而無法切出整齊的夾片。
* 除了用饅頭夾食外，亦可用土司或薄餅。

* Red fermented bean curd has a nice color and a strong flavor. Can be used as a meat tenderizer. It is rather salty, do not add too much. Add ketchup to have a better color and taste.
* Slightly freeze steamed breads for easier handling. Cut into thick slices. Split each almost all the way through, forming a pocket. Reheat in rice cooker.
* If you wish, substitute sliced white bread or Mandarin pancakes for steamed breads.

五香肉 Five Spice Pork

材料／
五花肉1條（約1斤重，5公分寬）、八角2粒、大蒜6粒、葱2支、薑1小塊
❶料：酒1大匙、醬油½杯、五香粉1茶匙、鹽½茶匙、糖½大匙
❷料：太白粉水1大匙

作法／
① 五花肉洗淨，放入電鍋內鍋，加開水2杯及切好的葱段、薑片，外鍋加水1杯，蒸至開關跳起時取出，將肉切成厚片（圖❶），肉湯2杯留用。
② 切好的肉以肉皮朝下，整齊排入碗內，再將❶料及肉湯調勻淋在肉面上，並放入拍碎的大蒜、八角後（圖❷），放入電鍋，外鍋加水2杯，蒸至開關跳起時取出。
③ 將蒸好的肉片挾入盤內，再將八角、大蒜揀淨，蒸肉的湯汁另用炒菜鍋燒開，並加❷料勾芡，黏稠時淋在肉面上即成。

INGREDIENTS/
1¹/₃ pounds fresh picnic pork shoulder, 2 star anise, 6 cloves garlic, 2 stalks green onion, 1 small piece ginger
❶ 1 T. cooking wine, 1/2 c. soy sauce, 1 t. five spice powder, 1/2 t. salt, 2 T. sugar
❷ 1 T. cornstarch solution

METHOD/
① Rinse pork shoulder, place in inner pan. Add 2 c. boiling water, sectioned green onion and sliced ginger. Add 1 c. water in rice cooker, steam until switch turns off. Remove. Cut pork into thick slices (fig. ❶). Reserve broth.
② Arrange sliced pork, skin side down, in serving bowl. Pour ❶ and broth over. Add smashed garlic and star anise (fig. ❷). Place in rice cooker. Add 2 c. water in rice cooker, steam until switch turns off. Remove.
③ Transfer sliced pork to serving platter, discard star anise and garlic. Pour liquid into wok, bring to boil. Thicken with ❷ Drizzle over pork.

紅醬豬肉 Red Sauce Pork

材料／
五花肉1斤、蒜2粒、薑1片
❶料：酒1大匙、紅腐乳汁3大匙、番茄醬3大匙、糖2大匙、鹽½茶匙、肉湯1杯
❷料：太白粉水½大匙、麻油少許

作法／
① 五花肉洗淨，放入電鍋，淋酒1大匙，加入薑片、開水2杯蓋過肉面，外鍋加水2杯，蒸至開關跳起。
② 將肉取出，在肉皮上下刀切成四方條（圖❶），皮朝下排在蒸碗內。
③ 將❶料調勻，澆在已放有大蒜之肉面（圖❷），再放入電鍋，外鍋加水2杯，蒸至開關跳起時取出。
④ 將紅醬豬肉之湯汁泌出，放炒鍋內，豬肉扣入盤中，再將湯汁燒開，用調味料❷勾芡後淋在豬肉上即成。食用時用蒸熱的饅頭切片夾食。

INGREDIENTS/
1¹/₃ pounds fresh picnic pork shoulder, boneless, 1 slice ginger, 2 cloves garlic
❶ 1 T. cooking wine, 3 T. fermented red bean curd juice, 3 T. ketchup, 2 T. sugar, 1/2 t. salt, 1 c. pork broth
❷ 1/2 T. cornstarch solution, dash sesame oil

METHOD/
① Rinse pork shoulder, place in inner pan. Add 1 T. cooking wine, ginger and 2 c. boiling water. Add 2 c. water in rice cooker, steam until switch turns off.
② Remove. Cut into thick rectangles (fig. ❶). Arrange pork, skin side down, in medium bowl.
③ Add garlic. Mix ❶. Pour over (fig. ❷). Place in rice cooker. Add 2 c. water in rice cooker, steam until switch turns off. Remove.
④ Carefully tip bowl, pour off liquid into wok. Bring to boil. Thicken with ❷. Invert bowl on serving platter, remove bowl. Drizzle sauce over pork. Serve with steamed bread slices.

* 香菇要選用週邊捲起成盒狀者爲佳，否則無法裝肉。
* 菇盒內先撒少許太白粉再放肉，才不易脫落。 * 香菇先單獨蒸熟，並入味後再鑲肉較好吃，否則鑲肉後無味。
* Choose dried black mushrooms with curved rims in order to hold stuffings.
* Sprinkle a little cornstarch inside of each mushroom. This will make mixture stick. * Steam black mushrooms before filling stuffings to have a better taste.

* 廣東臘味較甜，湖南臘味較鹹，若是鹹味重之臘味要鋪下多量糖與水同蒸，以去除過重之鹹味才可繼續後面的動作。
* 臘鴨脯較乾硬，故需先煮過再切，臘肉、臘腸較不硬，故蒸熟即可，但都要熟了再切，才不致變形及湯汁流失太多。
* Canton style salted meat has a sweet taste. Hunan style salted meat is rather salty. If using Hunan style salted pork and sausages, steam with some sugar and water in step ①.
* Salted duck meat is rather hard and dry. Cook in water before slicing. Slice salted pork and sausages after steaming it preverts meat from shrinking and losing juice.

菇盒鵪蛋 Quail Egg Stuffed Black Mushroom

材料／
香菇8朵、絞肉4兩、鵪鶉蛋8粒
❶料：酒½大匙、鹽¼茶匙、胡椒粉少許、太白粉1茶匙
❷料：醬油1大匙、糖1大匙、葱1支、薑2片、清水1杯
❸料：清水½杯、醬油½大匙、胡椒粉少許、太白粉水1大匙、麻油
少許

作法／
①香菇泡軟，絞肉剁細，拌入調味料❶調勻。
②香菇剪除菇蒂，加❷料（圖❶），先放入電鍋，外鍋加水1杯，蒸
至開關跳起時取出。
③待香菇稍涼時，瀝乾水分，在每朵內側撒少許乾太白粉，再放少
許絞肉，抹平後放上一粒鵪鶉蛋（圖❷）。
④全部作好放入電鍋，外鍋加水1杯蒸熟，開關跳起時取出，先移至
清潔盤內，另將湯汁倒入炒鍋，加入調味料❸炒黏稠，再淋回肉面
上即成。

INGREDIENTS/
8 dried black mushrooms, 6 oz. ground pork, 8 quail eggs
❶ 1/2 T. cooking wine, 1/4 t. salt, pinch white pepper, 1 t. cornstarch
❷ 1 T. soy sauce, 1 T. sugar, 1 stalk green onion, 2 slices ginger, 1 c. water
❸ 1/2 c. water, 1/2 T. soy sauce, pinch white pepper, 1 T. cornstarch
solution, dash sesame oil

METHOD/
① Soak dried black mushrooms in water to soften. Mince ground pork, stir in
、❶, mix well.
② Remove and discard black mushroom stems. Add ❷ (fig. ❶), place in rice
cooker. Add 1 c. water in rice cooker, steam until switch turns off. Remove.
③ Cool slightly. Drain. Dry-coat cavity with cornstarch. Fill with pork mixture.
Smooth surface. Place quail egg in center (fig. ❷). Place on plate.
④ Place in rice cooker. Add 1 c. water in rice cooker, steam until switch turns
off. Remove. Transfer to serving platter. Pour liquid into wok, add ❸, cook
until thickened. Pour over mushrooms.

臘味合 Salted Meat Combo

材料／
臘鴨脯1片、廣東臘肉1小塊、臘腸2條、葱2支、薑2片
❶料：酒1大匙、清水1杯
❷料：太白粉水1大匙、麻油少許

作法／
①先將臘鴨脯整塊煮熟（圖❶），然後切片，臘肉及臘腸則另外蒸熟
再切。
②用一個蒸碗，分別排入鴨脯、臘肉及臘腸，加入調味料❶（圖❷），
移入電鍋，外鍋加水1杯，蒸至開關跳起。
③將蒸好的臘味合取出，湯汁倒鍋內，臘味扣入盤內，再以調味料
❷將湯汁勾芡後，淋回肉面即成。

INGREDIENTS/
1 piece salted and dried duck meat, 1 small piece salted and dried pork, 2
links Chinese sausage, Canton style, 2 stalks green onion, 2 slices ginger
❶ 1 T. cooking wine, 1 c. water
❷ 1 T. cornstarch solution, dash sesame oil

METHOD/
① Cook salted duck meat in water until done (fig. ❶). Slice. Steam salted pork
and sausages until done, slice.
② Arrange duck, pork and sausage in medium bowl. Add ❶ (fig. ❷). Place in
rice cooker. Add 1 c. water in rice cooker, steam until switch turns off .
③ Remove. Carefully tip bowl, pour off liquid into wok. Invert bowl on serving
platter, remove bowl. Thicken liquid with ❷. Drizzle over salted meat.

蜜汁火腿 Honey-Glazed Ham

材料／

火腿（或家鄉肉）1斤、土司麵包½條

❶料：黃砂糖½斤

❷料：太白粉水1大匙

作法／

① 火腿用溫水刷洗淨外皮，放入電鍋內鍋，以水蓋過，外鍋加水2杯，蒸至開關跳起時取出。

② 稍涼時，將火腿切長片，排入蒸碗內，鋪上一層黃砂糖（½斤糖分三次用），加溫水½杯在火腿內，放入電鍋，外鍋加水2杯，蒸至開關跳起時取出，將水倒掉，鋪糖再蒸，如此反覆三次（圖❶）。

③ 土司麵包先修除四週硬邊，對切成長形，橫片成活頁狀（圖❷）。

④ 將第三次蒸好的火腿取出，湯汁倒在炒鍋內，火腿則扣入盤中，將湯汁加入❷料勾芡，黏稠時淋在火腿上。

⑤ 切好的土司麵包放電鍋內，加水½杯，蒸至開關跳起時取出，用以夾食蜜汁火腿。

INGREDIENTS/

1¹/₃ pounds Chinese ham, 1/2 loaf white bread, sliced

❶ 3/4 pound light brown sugar

❷ 1 T. cornstarch solution

METHOD/

① Brush ham surface under warm water. Place in inner pan, cover with water. Add 2 c. water in rice cooker, steam until switch turns off. Remove.

② Cool slightly. Cut into long slices. Arrange sliced ham in medium bowl. Sprinkle with 1/3 brown sugar on top. Place in rice cooker. Add 2 c. water in rice cooker. Steam until switch turns off. Remove and carefully pour off liquid. Sprinkle with another 1/3 brown sugar (fig. ❶), repeat this cooking procedure for 2 times.

③ Trim off bread crust and cut in half. Split each half almost all the way through lenghwise, forming a pocket (fig. ❷).
④ Remove bowl from rice cooker. Carefully tip bowl, pour off liquid into wok. Invert ham onto serving platter. Remove bowl. Thicken liquid with ❷. Pour over ham.
⑤ Place bread on plate, place in rice cooker. Add 1/2 c. water in rice cooker, steam until switch turns off. Remove. Serve with ham.

肉類

重點提示／REMARKS

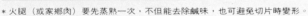

* 火腿（或家鄉肉）要先蒸熟一次，不但能去除鹹味，也可避免切片時變形。
* 土司麵包最好用冰箱冰硬或用隔夜的硬麵包，在去邊及片開時較容易達成，否則新鮮麵包太軟不好切。

* Substitute Virginia ham for Chinese ham if desired. The purpose of steaming ham in step ① is to remove excess salt and make slicing easier.
* Slightly freeze bread for easier handling.

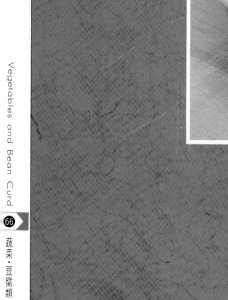

蔬菜・豆腐類　Vegetables & Bean Curd

重點提示／REMARKS

＊爲保存豆腐之水分，使質地細嫩及外形完整，豆腐買回後應泡水，用時再撈出。

＊豆腐鑲肉前，先撒少許乾粉，可防止絞肉脫落。 ＊豆腐蒸好後，泌出之湯汁爲豆腐水，無味，故不必留用，可以高湯另外勾芡，味道較好。

＊ Dry-coat indentations with cornstarch. This will make stuffings stick. ＊ The liquid from steaming bean curd has no flavor. Just discard.

＊除了用冬瓜外，也可以用大黃瓜以同樣方式烹調。 ＊蒸干貝之湯汁有鮮味，可代替高湯使用。

＊ Substitute cucumbers for winter melon, if desired. ＊ The liquid from steaming scallops has delicious flavor. If you wish, you may substitute it for soup stock.

金鑲白玉 Stuffed Bean Curd

材料╱
長形豆腐1塊、絞肉4兩、蝦米1大匙、葱1支
❶料：酒1大匙、醬油½大匙、鹽½茶匙、太白粉水½大匙
❷料：高湯1杯、蠔油2大匙、糖½茶匙、胡椒粉少許、太白粉水1大匙、麻油少許

作法╱
① 豆腐切長方形厚片，用小湯匙挖除中間少許，使之形成一凹洞（圖❶）。
② 絞肉剁細，蝦米泡軟切碎，混合後拌勻，並加❶料調味作成肉餡。
③ 每塊豆腐先在凹洞內撒少許乾太白粉，再填入肉餡少許，抹平（圖❷），放入電鍋，外鍋加水1杯，蒸至開關跳起時取出。
④ 將泌出之湯汁倒除，盛入乾淨盤內，另將❷料用炒鍋炒至黏稠時，淋在豆腐上即成。

INGREDIENTS/
1 cake regular Chinese style bean curd, 6 oz. ground pork, 1 T. dried shrimps, 1 stalk green onion
❶ 1 T. cooking wine, 1/2 T. soy sauce, 1/2 t. salt, 1/2 T. cornstarch solution
❷ 1 c. soup stock, 2 T. oyster-flavored sauce, 1/2 t. sugar, pinch white pepper, 1 T. cornstarch solution, dash sesame oil

METHOD/
① Cut bean curd into thick slice. Scoop out spoonful bean curd in center to make indentation (fig. ❶).
② Mince pork. Soak dried shrimps in water to soften. Mince finely. Mix pork, shrimp and ❶, mix well.
③ Sprinkle indentation with cornstarch. Stuff with pork mixture, smooth surface (fig. ❷). Place on plate. Place in rice cooker. Add 1 c. water in rice cooker, steam until switch turns off. Remove.
④ Transfer bean curd to serving platter, discard liquid. Heat wok with ❷, stir-fry until thickened. Drizzle over bean curd and serve.

干貝冬瓜球 Winter Melon with Dried Scallops

材料╱
冬瓜1½斤、干貝3粒
❶料：酒1大匙
❷料：高湯1杯、鹽1茶匙
❸料：太白粉水1大匙、麻油少許

作法╱
① 冬瓜去皮，用挖球器將冬瓜挖成球狀（圖❶），干貝泡水後，加❶料蒸熟。
② 將冬瓜球加❷料放入深碗（圖❷），移入電鍋，外鍋加水1杯，並將蒸熟之干貝撕碎，與冬瓜球同蒸至開關跳起時取出。
③ 將湯汁泌出，加❸料勾芡後淋回冬瓜球上即成。

INGREDIENTS/
2 pounds winter melon, 3 dried scallops
❶ 1 T. cooking wine
❷ 1 c. soup stock, 1 t. salt
❸ 1 T. cornstarch solution, dash sesame oil

METHOD/
① Pare winter melon, shape balls with melon baller (fig. ❶). Soak dried scallops in water to soften. Add ❶ steam until done.
② Place melon balls and ❷ in deep bowl (fig. ❷). Shred scallops by hand, Sprinkle over. Place in rice cooker. Add 1 c. water in rice cooker, steam until switch turns off. Remove.
③ Carefully tip bowl, pour off liquid into wok. Thicken with ❸. Drizzle over winter melon balls and serve.

蒸鑲茄段 Steamed Stuffed Eggplants

材料／
茄子3條、蔥1支、絞肉4兩
❶料：酒1大匙、醬油½大匙、
　鹽½茶匙、太白粉水½大匙
❷料：高湯（或清水）1杯、蠔
　油2大匙、糖1茶匙、太白粉
　水1大匙

作法／
①茄子洗淨，切5公分小段，並
　由中間切開一夾狀刀口（圖
　❶）。
②絞肉剁細，加入切碎之蔥末
　及❶料調成肉餡，每段茄子
　塞入肉餡少許（圖❷）。
③全部作好放入電鍋，外鍋加
　水1½杯，蒸至開關跳起時取
　出，倒除泌出之水分。
④將❷料燒開，澆在蒸好的茄
　段上即成。

INGREDIENTS/
3 Chinese eggplants, 1 stalk green
onion, 6 oz. ground pork
❶ 1 T. cooking wine, 1/2 T. soy
　sauce, 1/2 t. salt, 1/2 T. corn-
　starch solution
❷ 1 c. soup stock or water, 2 T.
　oyster-flavored sauce,1 t. sugar,
　1 T. cornstarch solution

METHOD/
① Rinse eggplants, cut into 2"
　sections. Split each almost all the
　way through lengthwise, forming
　a pocket (fig. ❶).
② Mince ground pork. Add minced
　green onion and ❶, mix well.
　Stuff into pockets (fig. ❷). Place
　on plate.
③ Place in rice cooker. Add 1½ c.
　water in rice cooker, steam until
　switch turns off. Remove. Discard
　liquid.
④ Heat wok with ❷, bring to boil.
　Pour over eggplants.

Vegetables and Bean Curd

蔬菜・豆腐類

重點提示／REMARKS

＊茄子鑲肉前，要先抹少許乾粉，以免肉餡脫落。
＊蒸好的茄段會分泌出水分，一定要倒除後再調味，否則會影響調味料之濃度。

＊ Dry-coat eggplant pockets with cornstarch. This will make stuffings stick.
＊ Discard the liquid from steaming which will thin the sauce.

重點提示／REMARKS

* 為避免臭豆腐之氣味留在電鍋內，入鍋之前，不妨先包一層保潔膜再蒸。 * 與臭豆腐同蒸的配料，除蔥花、辣椒外，亦可用煮熟的毛豆與火腿屑。
* Cover the inner pot with plastic wrap before placing in rice cooker, if you don't want the rice cooker to absorb the strong smell.
* In step ①, add tender soybeans or minced Virginia ham to odorous fermented bean curds, if desired.

* 沒有肉醬罐頭時，可用炒香的絞肉代替。 * 蒸好的豆腐會出一點水，一定要與肉醬再拌勻調味才較平均且入味。
* Substitute stir-fried ground pork for pork paste, if desired. * Before serving, make sure the pork paste and the bean curd are blended well.

肉醬蒸豆腐 Steamed Bean Curd with Pork Paste

材料／
長形豆腐1塊、肉醬罐頭1罐、葱1支
❶料：蠔油1大匙、糖½茶匙、胡椒粉少許
作法／
①長形豆腐修除硬邊，切丁，放蒸盤內（圖❶）。
②肉醬罐頭打開，將肉醬倒出，與❶料混合。
③調勻的肉醬澆在豆腐上（圖❷），放入電鍋，外鍋加水1杯，蒸至
　開關跳起時取出，略微拌勻，盛入乾淨盤內，撒下切好的葱花即成。

INGREDIENTS/
**1 cake regular Chinese style bean curd, 1 can pork paste, 1 stalk green
onion**
❶ 1 T. oyster-flavored sauce, 1/2 t. sugar, pinch white pepper
METHOD/
① Dice bean curd. Place on plate (fig. ❶).
② Mix pork paste and ❶.
③ Pour over bean curd (fig. ❷). Place in rice cooker. Add 1 c. water in rice
　cooker, steam until switch turns off. Remove. Stir. Transfer to serving platter.
　Sprinkle with chopped green onion and serve.

蒸臭豆腐 Steamed Odorous Fermented Bean Curd

材料／
臭豆腐4片、葱1支、辣椒1支
❶料：酒½大匙、醬油1大匙、麻油1大匙、味精少許
作法／
①臭豆腐洗淨，放蒸盤內，鋪下切碎的葱粒及辣椒（圖❶）。
②將❶料調勻，淋在臭豆腐上，放入電鍋，外鍋加水1杯，蒸至開關
　跳起時取出即成。

INGREDIENTS/
4 odorous fermented bean curds, 1 stalk green onion, 1 fresh chili pepper
❶ 1/2 T. cooking wine, 1 T. soy sauce, 1 T. sesame oil, pinch MSG
METHOD/
① Wash odorous fermented bean curds, place on plate. Sprinkle with minced
　green onion and minced chili pepper (fig. ❶).
② Mix ❶, drizzle over fermented bean curd. Place in rice cooker. Add 1 c.
　water in rice cooker, steam until switch turns off. Remove and serve.

重點提示／REMARKS

* 東洋魚即醃漬過之日本鹹鰱魚，可在雜貨店買到，色澤微紅，蒸豆腐有配色效果。
* 東洋魚一定要蒸過再用，可去腥亦去鹹，但要放涼再切，魚肉才不會碎掉。
* Japanese style salted fish is pink-colored salted silver carp. Available in Oriental markets.
* In step ②, steam salted fish to remove salty taste and fishy odor. Cool fish before slicing, otherwise, it will fall apart.

* 亦可在調味中加少許蔥花配色。　* 切好的茄子用鹽水浸過，色澤不會變黑。
* 蒸好的茄子易出水，水要倒除，調味料要濃一點，茄子涼後才不會因湯汁泌出而使調味料變稀。
* Garnish with chopped green onion, if desired.
* Soak sectioned eggplants in salted water to prevent them from browning.　* Discard the liquid from steaming which will thin the sauce.

洋魚豆腐夾 Salted Fish Stuffed Bean Curd

材料／
東洋魚1小塊、長形豆腐1塊、葱1支
❶料：酒1大匙、清水1杯
❷料：高湯1杯、鹽½茶匙、胡椒粉少許、太白粉水1大匙、麻油少許
作法／
①豆腐洗淨，切厚片，再由中間片開成活頁夾（圖❶）。
②東洋魚洗淨，加❶料，先放入電鍋，外鍋加水1杯，蒸至開關跳起時取出，將水倒除，洋魚放涼後片開，剔除大骨及魚皮，切與豆腐同長度之薄片（圖❷）。
③將魚肉夾入豆腐內，放入電鍋，外鍋加水½杯，蒸至開關跳起時取出。
④將豆腐泌出之湯汁倒除，另用❷料燒開，勾芡成黏稠狀時淋在洋魚豆腐夾上，並撒下切碎之葱花即成。

INGREDIENTS/
1 small piece Japanese style salted fish, 1 cake regular Chinese style bean curd, 1 stalk green onion
❶ 1 T. cooking wine, 1 c. water
❷ 1 c. soup stock, 1/2 t. salt, pinch white pepper, 1 T. cornstarch solution, dash sesame oil
METHOD/
① Rinse bean curd, cut into thick slices. Split each almost all the way through lengthwise, forming pocket (fig. ❶).
② Rinse salted fish, add ❶. Place in rice cooker. Add 1 c. water in rice cooker steam until switch turns off. Remove. Discard liquid. Cool. Remove and discard bones and skin. Cut into thin slices (fig. ❷).
③ Stuff fish slices into bean curd pockets. Place in rice cooker. Add 1/2 c. water in rice cooker, steam until switch turns off. Remove.
④ Discard liquid. Heat wok with ❷, bring to boil. Cook until thickened. Pour over stuffed bean curd. Sprinkle with chopped green onion and serve.

蒜茸茄子 Eggplants with Minced Garlic

材料／
茄子3條、大蒜3粒
❶料：醬油1大匙、蠔油2大匙、糖1大匙、麻油1大匙
作法／
①茄子洗淨，先切小段，再一剖為二（圖❶）。
②將茄子放入鹽水中浸泡3分鐘後撈出（圖❷），瀝乾水分，放入蒸盤，外鍋加水1杯，蒸至開關跳起時取出放涼。
③大蒜搗碎、切細，加入❶料調勻，淋在茄子上即成。

INGREDIENTS/
3 Chinese eggplants, 3 cloves garlic
❶ 1 T. soy sauce, 2 T. oyster-flavored sauce, 1 T. sugar, 1 T. sesame oil
METHOD/
① Rinse eggplants, cut into small sections. Halve lengthwise (fig. ❶).
② Soak in salted water for 3 minutes, remove (fig. ❷). Drain, place on plate. Place in rice cooker. Add 1 c. water in rice cooker, steam until switch turns off. Remove. Cool.
③ Mince garlic, add ❶. Mix well. Drizzle over eggplants and serve.

Vegetables and Bean Curd

蔬菜・豆腐類

茶碗蒸 Savory Steamed Eggs

材料／
蛋4個、香菇4朵、魚板½條
❶料：冷高湯2杯、鹽1茶匙
作法／
①蛋打散，加入❶料拌勻（圖
　❶），盛入蒸碗內。
②放入電鍋，外鍋加水2杯，先
　蒸5分鐘，再放入泡軟切片的
　香菇及魚板(圖❷)。
③繼續蒸至開關跳起時即取
　出。

INGREDIENTS/
4 eggs, 4 dried black mushrooms,
1/2 steamed fish cake (kamaboko)
❶ 2 c. cold soup stock, 1 t. salt
METHOD/
① Whisk eggs lightly. Add ❶, mix
　well (fig. ❶). Pour into deep bowl.
② Place in rice cooker. Add 2 c.
　water in rice cooker, steam for 5
　minutes. Add softened and sliced
　black mushrooms and sliced fish
　cake (fig. ❷).
③ Steam until switch turns off.
　Remove.

重點提示

＊除了香菇及魚板外，配料還可用蛤蜊、蝦仁和雞肉。
＊不可一開始就將配料放入蛋汁內同蒸，否則會沉底，最好待蛋液稍凝固時再放入
＊蒸蛋時最好加一鐵架將蒸碗架高，不要直接接觸鍋底，中途要將鍋蓋留一縫隙，
　避免熱度太高造成蒸好的蛋有蜂窩

Vegetables and Bean Curd

蔬菜・豆腐類

REMARKS

* Add clams, shrimps, or sliced chicken, if desired.
* In step ②, add black mushrooms and fish cake when the top of egg mixture is just set.
  This will avoid them from sinking.
* Place deep bowl on rack in rice cooker. In the middle of steaming, leave the cover ajar.
  This will avoid the honeycomb-like texture in the steamed eggs.

* 燉雞湯一定要用開水，不但傳熱快，也避免肉質內剩餘之血水再流出，而使湯汁混濁。
* 泡香菇的水也有香味，可以再利用，不妨倒入鍋內一同蒸雞。
* In step ③, cook chicken in boiling water to have a clear broth. * If you wish, keep the water from soaking black mushrooms. Add in inner pan in step ③.

* 雞爪以購買肉雞之雞爪較肥嫩，土雞及半土雞太瘦長，無肉。
* Chicken feet are available in Oriental markets.

紅棗香菇雞湯 Chicken Soup with Red Dates and Black Mushrooms

材料／

雞腿2隻、紅棗20粒、香菇10朵、薑1小塊

❶料：酒1大匙、鹽½茶匙

作法／

①雞腿剁小塊，放入冷水中煮開，燙除血水後撈出，沖淨泡沫（圖❶）。

②香菇、紅棗洗淨，泡水，並將香菇蒂剪除（圖❷）。

③將所有材料放入電鍋內鍋，並加入開水6杯及酒1大匙，外鍋加水3杯，蒸至開關跳起時，加鹽調味，即可盛出食用。

INGREDIENTS/

2 chicken legs, 20 dried red dates, 10 dried black mushrooms, 1 small piece ginger
❶ 1 T. cooking wine, 1/2 t. salt

METHOD/

① Rinse chicken legs, chop into small pieces. Cover with water, bring to boil. Drain, rinse to remove scum (fig. ❶).

② Rinse red dates, soak in water. Rinse black mushrooms, soak in water to soften. Remove and discard stems (fig. ❷).

③ Place chicken, red dates, black mushrooms, 1 T. cooking wine and 6 c. boiling water in inner pan. Place in rice cooker. Add 3 c. water in rice cooker, steam until switch turns off. Stir in salt. Ready to serve.

金鈎鳳爪湯 Soybean Sprouts and Chicken Feet Soup

材料／

黃豆芽½斤、雞爪12隻、薑1小塊

❶料：酒1大匙、鹽1茶匙、麻油少許

作法／

①將雞爪爪尖剁除（圖❶），黃豆芽摘除根部，洗淨。

②雞爪放冷水內煮開，撈出後沖淨泡沫瀝乾（圖❷），放入電鍋內鍋並加開水8杯及薑片、酒1大匙，移入電鍋，外鍋加水4杯燉20分鐘。

③加入黃豆芽，繼續燉至開關跳起時加鹽調味即可移出，盛入湯碗內時再滴麻油少許即可。

INGREDIENTS/

2/3 pound soybean sprouts, 12 chicken feet, 1 small piece ginger
❶ 1 T. cooking wine, 1 t. salt, dash sesame oil

METHOD/

① Chop off nails from chicken feet (fig. ❶). Remove and discard roots from soybean sprouts, rinse well.

② Cover chicken feet with water, bring to boil. Drain, rinse to remove scum (fig. ❷). Place in inner pan, add 8 c. boiling water, sliced ginger and 1 T. cooking wine. Place in rice cooker. Add 4 c. water in rice cooker, steam for 20 minutes.

③ Add soybean sprouts, steam until switch turns off. Stir in salt. Pour into serving bowl. Add sesame oil and serve.

* 苦瓜鑲肉前要先抹少許乾太白粉，鑲好的肉才不會脫落。
* 先將苦瓜鑲肉蒸過，使其定型後再放入湯內同蒸，才可保持湯汁清爽，否則會因絞肉的血水滲出而影響湯汁色澤。
* Dry-coat inside of bitter melon with cornstarch. This will make stuffings stick.　* Steam stuffed bitter melon before adding to soup stock in order to make a clear soup.

* 豬肚小的話一次用一個，豬肚大只需半個即可。
* 如買煮熟的豬肚時，作法①②即可省略，或是一次多處理幾個豬肚，蒸熟後放冷凍庫，下次直接取用即可，那就省事多了。
* 湯蒸好後調味前要先試試味道，再決定是否加鹽，因為酸菜心本身鹹，久蒸可使鹹味流出於湯內。
* If you wish, you may cook a few pork tripes at a time. Use one and freeze others for future use.
* Pickled mustard heart is rather salty. Taste soup before adding salt.

苦瓜鑲肉湯 Pork Stuffed Bitter Melon Soup

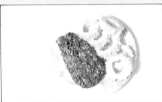

材料／
苦瓜1條、絞肉10兩
❶料：酒1大匙、鹽1茶匙、胡椒粉少許、太白粉水1大匙
❷料：高湯5杯、鹽1茶匙、麻油少許
作法／
①苦瓜洗淨，橫切成5公分寬之圈狀，絞肉再剁細（圖❶）。
②在每圈苦瓜內側瓜瓤處先抹少許乾太白粉（圖❷）。
③絞肉拌入❶料調勻後，在每圈苦瓜塞入絞肉少許，抹平放蒸盤內，再移入電鍋，外鍋加水1杯，蒸至開關跳起時取出。
④將❷料放大碗內，並放入蒸好的苦瓜鑲肉，再移入電鍋，外鍋加水2½杯，蒸至開關跳起時取出即可。

INGREDIENTS/
1 bitter melon, 3/4 pound ground pork
❶ 1 T. cooking wine, 1 t. salt, pinch white pepper, 1 T. cornstarch solution
❷ 5 c. soup stock, 1 t. salt, dash sesame oil

METHOD/
① Rinse bitter melon. Cut into 2" inch slices. Remove seeds. Mince ground pork (fig. ❶).
② Coat inside of bitter melon with cornstarch (fig. ❷).
③ Mix minced ground pork and ❶, stuff into bitter melon, smooth surface. Place on plate. Place in rice cooker. Add 1 c. water in rice cooker, steam until switch turns off. Remove.
④ Place ❷ in large bowl, add stuffed bitter melon. Place in rice cooker. Add 2¹/₂ c. water in rice cooker, steam until switch turns off. Remove and serve.

酸菜肚片湯 Pickled Mustard and Pork Tripe Soup

材料／
豬肚1個、酸菜心5片、薑1小塊
❶料：高湯5杯、酒1大匙、鹽½茶匙
作法／
①豬肚買回先沖淨，再以麵粉1杯、沙拉油2大匙揉搓，洗去黏液後以水沖淨，再用2大匙酒、2大匙醋揉搓，洗除腥臭味，沖淨。
②將豬肚放入電鍋內鍋，加水5杯及酒1大匙、薑2片，外鍋加水5杯，蒸至開關跳起時取出豬肚。
③豬肚放涼後切片（圖❶），薑切絲，一同放入電鍋內鍋，並加入❶料中之高湯及酒，移入電鍋，外鍋加水4杯先蒸半小時。
④酸菜心洗淨，切片（圖❷），待肚片已熟爛再放入同蒸，直至開關跳起時，加鹽調味後盛出即可。

INGREDIENTS/
1 pork tripe, 5 leaves pickled mustard heart, 1 small piece ginger
❶ 5 c. soup stock, 1 T. cooking wine, 1/2 t. salt

METHOD/
① Wash pork tripe. Rub with 1 c. flour and 2 T. oil, rinse well. Add 2 T. cooking wine and 2 T. vinegar, rub well, rinse.
② Place tripe in inner pan, add 5 c. water, 1 T. cooking wine and 2 slices ginger. Place in rice cooker. Add 5 c. water in rice cooker, steam until switch turns off. Remove tripe.
③ Cool. Slice (fig. ❶). Shred ginger. Place sliced tripe and shredded ginger in inner pan, add soup stock and cooking wine. Place in rice cooker. Add 4 c. water in rice cooker, steam for 30 minutes.
④ Rinse pickled mustard heart, slice (fig. ❷). Add to tripe. Cook until switch turns off. Stir in salt. Remove and serve.

* 一定要用開水燉魚，湯汁才清爽，或將魚塊尖燙過再蒸亦可。
* 木瓜不要買過熟的，以免蒸後太爛影響湯汁清爽，若使用生木瓜，一開始就要放入與生魚同燉。　* 亦可添加西洋參數片提味。
* Steam fish in boiling water to have a clear soup. If you wish, blanch fish in boiling water before steaming to have the same result.
* In order to keep the soup clear, do not use papaya which is overripe. If using unripe papaya, steam with fish in step ②.
* Add a few slices of ginseng if desired.

* 虱目魚肚較肥嫩，且刺少，所有小刺均集中於背部，故食用時要注意魚背的刺。
* 虱目魚的魚腹內有油脂，清洗時不要刮除，洗淨即可。　* 亦可添加醃鳳梨、醃冬瓜同蒸，風味亦佳。
* Milkfish is quite bony. There are many tiny bones along back.
* When cleaning milkfish, do not remove the fat in stomach. * Steam fish with preserved pineapple or preserved winter melon to have a different taste.

杏仁木瓜湯 Almonds and Papaya Soup

材料／
生魚1條（12兩到1斤，又名鱧魚）、小型木瓜1個、杏仁½杯
❶料：酒1大匙、鹽1茶匙
作法／
① 生魚洗淨，切小段（圖❶），木瓜去皮，切大粗塊，杏仁用水浸泡半小時。
② 將生魚與杏仁放入電鍋內鍋，並加入開水6杯（圖❷），淋酒1大匙，外鍋加水3杯開始蒸。
③ 20分鐘後放入木瓜同蒸，直至開關跳起時取出，加鹽調味後即可食用。

INGREDIENTS/
1 whole catfish, 1 small papaya, 1/2 c. almonds
❶ 1 T. cooking wine, 1/2 t. salt
METHOD/
① Rinse catfish, cut into small sections (fig. ❶). Pare papaya, cut into large pieces (fig. ❷). Soak almonds in water for 30 minutes.
② Place fish and almonds in inner pan, add 6 c. boiling water and 1 T. cooking wine. Place in rice cooker. Add 3 c. water in rice cooker, steam for 20 minutes.
③ Add papaya, steam until switch turns off. Stir in salt. Remove and serve.

虱目魚湯 Milkfish Soup

材料／
虱目魚1條（約1斤2兩）、薑1小塊
❶料：酒1大匙、鹽1茶匙
作法／
① 虱目魚洗淨，先切下頭部，再將魚尾修齊，由中間下刀切開魚腹及背，分兩段（圖❶），再切成小塊。
② 電鍋內鍋先放開水6杯及薑絲並淋酒1大匙後，再將切好的虱目魚塊放入（圖❷）。
③ 電鍋外鍋加水1½杯，蒸至開關跳起時加鹽調味，即可盛出食用。

INGREDIENTS/
1 milkfish, 1 small piece ginger
❶ 1 T. cooking wine, 1 t. salt
METHOD/
① Rinse fish. Remove head, trim off tail. Cut in half (fig. ❶).
② Place 6 c. boiling water, shredded ginger and 1 T. cooking wine in inner pan. Add fish (fig. ❷).
③ Add 1½ c. water in rice cooker, steam until switch turns off. Stir in salt. Remove and serve.

清湯雙捲 Double Rolls Soup

材料／
絞肉10兩、高麗菜葉8片、百頁1疊
❶料：酒1大匙、蔥薑水3大匙、鹽1茶匙、胡椒粉少許、太白粉水1大匙
❷料：高湯6杯，鹽1茶匙，麻油、胡椒粉少許

作法／
①絞肉剁細，拌入❶料調勻作成肉餡，百頁、高麗菜分別用開水汆燙過撈出（圖❶）。
②高麗菜燙軟後，將葉梗切除少許（圖❷），和百頁分別包入肉餡後，捲成條狀。
③將捲好的高麗菜捲和百頁捲排入蒸碗內（圖❸），加入❷料中的高湯及鹽，放入電鍋，外鍋加水2杯，蒸至開關跳起時取出即可。食用時加麻油和胡椒粉即成。

INGREDIENTS/
3/4 pound ground pork, 8 cabbage leaves, 10 dried bean curd sheets
❶ 1 T. cooking wine, 3 T. green onion and ginger water, 1 t. salt, pinch white pepper, 1 T. corn-starch solution
❷ 6 c. soup stock, 1 t. salt, pinch white pepper, dash sesame oil

METHOD/
① Mince ground pork, stir in ❶, mix well. Blanch dried bean curd sheets and cabbage leaves in boiling water separately. Remove (fig. ❶).
② Trim off hard leafstalks from cabbage (fig. ❷). Put some meat mixture on bean curd sheet and cabbage leaf. Wrap up.
③ Arrange rolls in deep bowl (fig. ❸). Add soup stock and salt. Place in rice cooker. Add 2 c. water in rice cooker, steam until switch turns off. Remove. Sprinkle with pepper. Add sesame oil and serve.

重點提示／REMARKS

* 燙百頁時，要在水裏加少許小蘇打使其軟化，並有漂白功能，但要注意時間，不可жи燙過久，以免過爛。
* 包捲高麗菜時，一定要先將硬梗切除少許再包，否則不易平整。
* 雙捲放入蒸碗內時，記得要將封口朝下或兩面重疊，以免蒸氣將封口掀開。

---

* When blanching dried bean curd sheets, add some baking soda in boiling water. Don't blanch for too long. Otherwise, they will break into pieces.
* Trim off hard leafstalks from cabbage before wrapping for easy handling.
* In step ③, place rolls, seam side down, in deep bowl.

重點提示／REMARKS

* 選購鴨肉時，以鴨胸脯結實者為佳，肉質厚實有彈性，若鴨胸脯柔嫩者，肉質亦鬆軟，腥味重。
* 冬菜有特別香氣，但極易含沙，故需仔細清洗，但不可浸泡太久，以免香味消失。
* When selecting duck, press duck breast to make sure it is firm and not soggy.
* Rinse preserved vegetables well in case there is any dirt. Soak too long will lose flavor.

* 牛肉整塊蒸熟再切，肉質較嫩，可避免肉汁鮮味流失在湯內，肉塊亦整齊，不會因加熱而變形。
* 燉湯的牛肉以肋條和裏脊邊兩部位較適合，牛腱亦可，但肉太瘦且筋多，口感較澀硬。
* 燉好的牛肉不要立刻離鍋端出，稍燜一會兒可使肉質更軟爛、蘿蔔更透而不致夾生，但不可加鹽同蒸，否則會變硬燉不爛。
* Cook beef before slicing to prevent beef from shrinking. Besides, the texture will be tenderer.
* Use brisket or skirt steak for soup. Beef shank, which is too lean and has too much gristle, is not the first choise.
* Let beef soup stand in rice cooker for a while after switch turns off. Both beef and radish will be tenderer. Do not add salt before steaming. Otherwise, the texture of beef will be tough.

冬菜鴨湯 Duck Soup with Preserved Vegetables

材料╱
鴨½隻(約1½斤)、薑1小塊、冬菜1杯
❶料：酒1大匙、鹽1茶匙、胡椒粉少許
作法╱
①鴨洗淨，剁小塊，先汆燙過一次，去除血水後撈出，沖淨（圖❶）。
②薑切片，和鴨肉一同放入電鍋內鍋，外鍋加水4杯，並加❶料的酒同蒸（圖❷）。
③冬菜洗淨，見鴨肉已爛時再放入，蒸至開關跳起時，加鹽調味取出。
④食用時揀除薑片，撒胡椒粉少許即可。

INGREDIENTS/
1/2 duck, 1 small piece ginger, 1 c. preserved vegetables
❶ 1 T. cooking wine, 1 t. salt, pinch white pepper
METHOD/
① Rinse duck, chop into small pieces. Blanch in boiling water to remove scum. Drain, rinse (fig. ❶).
② Slice ginger. Place duck, sliced ginger and cooking wine in inner pan. Place in rice cooker. Add 4 c. water in rice cooker (fig. ❷), steam until duck is tender.
③ Rinse preserved vegetables, add to duck, cook until switch turns off. Stir in salt. Remove.
④ Remove and discard sliced ginger. Sprinkle with white pepper and serve.

清燉牛肉湯 Beef Soup

材料╱
牛肋條肉1½斤、蘿蔔1條、薑4片
❶料：酒2大匙、鹽1茶匙、胡椒粉少許
作法╱
①牛肋條洗淨，整塊汆燙過血水後沖淨，放入電鍋內鍋，加水6杯蓋過牛肉，並加薑4片、酒1大匙，外鍋加水3杯，蒸至開關跳起時取出，撈出牛肉放涼（圖❶）。
②蘿蔔去皮切小塊，牛肉切塊（圖❷），再放入電鍋內鍋，連同牛肉湯，再淋酒1大匙同蒸，外鍋加水3杯，蒸至開關跳起時，加鹽調味。
③食用時再撒少許胡椒粉即可。

INGREDIENTS/
2 pounds skirt steak, 1 Chinese radish, 1 small piece ginger
❶ 2 T. cooking wine, 1 t. salt, pinch white pepper
METHOD/
① Rinse beef. Blanch in boiling water to remove scum. Rinse. Place in inner pan, add 6 c. water, 4 slices ginger and 1 T. cooking wine. Place in rice cooker. Add 3 c. water in rice cooker, steam until switch turns off. Remove beef. Cool (fig. ❶). Reserve beef broth.
② Pare Chinese radish, cut into small pieces. Cut beef into pieces (fig. ❷). Place radish and beef in inner pan with reserved beef broth and 1 T. cooking wine. Add 3 c. water in rice cooker, steam until switch turns off. Stir in salt.
③ Sprinkle with white pepper and serve.

重點提示／REMARKS

* 西瓜當容器有特別的清香味，但不耐久蒸，故需先將雞肉蒸熟再放入，吸取其氣味即可，以免同蒸易使西瓜破裂。
* 西瓜放入電鍋蒸時也要先用一個容器裝盛，不可直接放入。 * 為使西瓜平穩站立，可在底部切平少許，即可防止傾斜而導致湯汁溢出。
* Using watermelon as a serving container gives the soup a pleasant flavor. Do not steam watermelon too long, it will crack.
* Set melon in deep bowl to hold it in place. Then place in rice cooker. * In order to prevent tipping, you may flatten the bottom by trimming off some melon.

---

* 汽鍋是一種容器內部有一根具通汽功能的汽柱，可吸收蒸汽，使食物在致熟過程中，具有蒸與煮特色的烹調鍋，材質有砂、陶、瓷三種。
* 由於汽鍋的汽柱是內外相通的，所以放入電鍋蒸時，一定要先用鐵架架高，不可直接沉在水裏蒸，以免外鍋水經由汽柱灌入湯鍋內。
* 除了雞腿，也可以用雞肉或鴨肉來做。
* Yunnan pot has a central chimney which allows the food inside to be steamed and boiled at the same time. Made of sand, clay, or porcelain.
* Place Yunnan pot on rack in rice cooker without touching the water in rice cooker. Otherwise, the water will go back to the pot through the chimney.
* Substitute duck or frying chicken for chicken legs.

神仙西瓜雞 Chicken Watermelon Soup

材料／
雞腿2隻、筍2支、香菇5朵、小西瓜1個
❶料：酒1大匙、鹽1茶匙
作法／
①雞腿洗淨，剁小塊（圖❶），先氽燙過，以去除血水，再沖淨備用。
②西瓜先切除蒂頭約5公分左右，作成蓋子，再將中間瓜肉挖除（圖❷）。
③先將雞腿、切好的筍條及泡軟、去蒂、切條的香菇，一同放入電鍋內鍋，並加❶料同蒸，外鍋加水2杯，蒸至開關跳起時取出。
④將已先蒸過的雞腿料倒入西瓜盅內，放入電鍋，外鍋加水1杯再蒸，直至開關跳起時再取出。

INGREDIENTS/
2 chicken legs, 2 bamboo shoots, 5 dried black mushrooms, 1 small whole watermelon
❶ 1 T. cooking wine, 1/2 t. salt
METHOD/
① Rinse chicken legs, chop into small pieces (fig. ❶). Blanch in boiling water to remove scum. Rinse.
② Cut about 2" melon off top as cap. Scrape out seeds and pulp (fig. ❷).
③ Cut bamboo shoots into thick strips. Soak dried black mushrooms in water to soften. Remove stems. Cut into strips. Place chicken, bamboo shoots, black mushrooms and ❶ in inner pan. Place in rice cooker. Add 2 c. water in rice cooker, steam until switch turns off. Remove.
④ Pour into melon. Place melon in rice cooker. Add 1 c. water in rice cooker, steam until switch turns off. Remove and serve.

汽鍋雞湯 Chicken Soup in Yunnan Pot

材料／
雞腿2隻、冬筍2支、香菇5朵、火腿4兩
❶料：酒1大匙、鹽½茶匙、胡椒粉少許
作法／
①雞腿洗淨，剁小塊，先氽燙過以去除血水後沖淨備用（圖❶）。
②火腿先煮一次以去除鹹味，並於煮熟後切粗條，冬筍切條，香菇泡軟、去蒂、對切兩半，全部材料放入汽鍋內，並加入雞腿（圖❷），淋酒1大匙，再加開水4杯同蒸。
③外鍋加水4杯，再放一鐵架墊高，然後才放入汽鍋，蒸至開關跳起時取出，再加鹽調味即可，食用時再撒胡椒粉。

INGREDIENTS/
2 chicken legs, 2 bamboo shoots, 5 dried black mushrooms, 6 oz. Chinese ham or Virginia ham
❶ 1 T. cooking wine, 1/2 t. salt, pinch white pepper
METHOD/
① Rinse chicken legs, chop into small pieces. Blanch in boiling water to remove scum. Rinse (fig. ❶).
② Cook ham in water until done to remove salty taste. Cut into thick strips. Cut bamboo shoots into thick strips. Soak dried black mushrooms in water to soften. Remove stems. Cut in half. Place chicken, ham, bamboo shoots, black mushrooms (fig. ❷), 1 T. cooking wine, and 4 c. boiling water in Yunnan pot.
③ Set rack in rice cooker, add 4 c. water. Place Yunnan pot in rice cooker, steam until switch turns off. Remove. Stir in salt. Sprinkle with white pepper and serve.

重點提示／REMARKS

* 雞腿蒸熟再去骨切條，才可保持湯汁清爽，避免血水流出及肉質因加熱而變形。
* 瓠瓜絲不可泡水太久，以免易斷，用水浸濕即可使用。 * 除雞腿外，亦可用鴨肉，做法與雞腿的處理方式相同。
* Precook chicken leg before cutting into strips. The soup will retain clear and the meat will not shrink.
* Do not soak dried gourd strips in water for too long. Just wet them. * Substitute duck meat for chicken leg, if desired.

* 青剛菜燙熟後沖冷水，可保持色澤翠綠，不變黃。 * 餛飩另外用開水煮熟再撈入湯內，可保持湯汁清爽不混濁，口感亦較富彈性。
* The purpose of rinsing blanched baby bok choy in cold water is to retain its fresh color. * In order to have a clear soup, precook won tons before adding to the soup.

柴把雞湯 Firewood Bundle Chicken Soup

材料／
雞腿1隻、酸菜心4片、筍1支、香菇5朵、瓠瓜絲1兩
❶料：酒1大匙、薑2片、開水6杯
❷料：高湯6杯、鹽1茶匙、胡椒粉少許

作法／
①雞腿洗淨，先燙除血水後，加❶料放入電鍋內鍋，外鍋加水2杯，蒸至開關跳起時取出（圖❶），撈出雞腿放涼。
②將雞腿去骨後切粗條，筍煮熟切條，酸菜心切條，香菇泡軟、去蒂切條，瓠瓜絲泡濕切長段。
③各種材料各取一條，用瓠瓜絲綑綁成柴把狀（圖❷），放入電鍋內鍋，並加❷料同蒸，外鍋加水2杯，蒸至開關跳起時取出即可食用。

INGREDIENTS/
1 chicken leg, 4 leaves pickled mustard heart, 1 bamboo shoot, 5 dried black mushrooms, 1½ oz. dried gourd strips
❶ 1 T. cooking wine, 2 slices ginger, 6 c. boiling water
❷ 6 c. soup stock, 1 t. salt, pinch white pepper
METHOD/
① Rinse chicken leg blanch in boiling water to remove scum. Place in inner pan, add ❶. Add 2 c. water in rice cooker, steam until switch turns off. Remove (fig. ❶). Remove chicken leg cool.
② Remove and discard chicken bones. Cut into thick strips. Cook bamboo shoot in water until done, cut into thick strips. Cut pickled mustard heart into thick strips. Soak dried black mushrooms in water to soften. Remove stems, cut into thick strips. Soak dried gourd strips in water to wet. Cut into long sections.
③ Take one of each chicken, bamboo shoot, mustard heart and black mushroom, tie together with gourd strip to make bundle (fig. ❷). Place in inner pan, add ❷. Add 2 c. water in rice cooker, steam until switch turns off. Remove and serve.

餛飩鴨湯 Won Ton Duck Soup

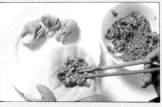

材料／
鴨½隻、絞肉6兩、餛飩皮2兩、青剛菜10棵
❶料：酒1大匙、蔥1支、薑2片、開水10杯
❷料：酒½大匙、鹽½茶匙、太白粉水½大匙
❸料：鹽2茶匙、胡椒粉少許

作法／
①鴨洗淨，剁小塊，先汆燙過血水，然後沖淨泡沫備用（圖❶）。
②將鴨肉放入電鍋內鍋，加入❶料，外鍋加水5杯蒸至鴨肉熟爛。
③絞肉剁細，並加入❷料調勻成肉餡，然後每張餛飩皮包入餡料少許，作成餛飩（圖❷）。
④水半鍋燒開，先汆燙洗淨的青剛菜，一熟即撈出以冷水沖涼，再放入餛飩，煮熟即撈出，一同放入鴨湯內，並加❸料調味，蒸至開關跳起即移出食用，同時揀除蔥、薑。

INGREDIENTS/
1/2 duck, 1/2 pound ground pork, 3 oz. won ton wrappers, 10 baby bok choy
❶ 1 T. cooking wine, 1 stalk green onion, 2 slices ginger, 10 c. boiling water
❷ 1/2 T. cooking wine, 1/2 t. salt, 1/2 T. cornstarch solution
❸ 2 t. salt, pinch white pepper
METHOD/
① Rinse duck, chop into small pieces. Blanch in boiling water to remove scum. Rinse (fig. ❶).
② Place duck in inner pan, add ❶. Add 5 c. water in rice cooker, steam until duck is done.
③ Mince ground pork. Stir in ❷, mix well. Place some pork mixture on won ton wrapper. Fold well (fig. ❷).
④ Blanch baby bok choy in boiling water, cook until done. Remove immediately. Rinse under cold running water. Drain. Add won tons in boiling water, cook until done. Remove. Place bok choy and won tons in duck soup. Add ❸ to taste. Steam until switch turns off. Remove and discard green onion and ginger. Ready to serve.

材料／

豬肚1個、筍1支、香菇10朵、
紅棗1兩

❶料：酒1大匙、蔥1支、薑2片

❷料：高湯6杯、酒1大匙、鹽
1茶匙

作法／

①豬肚洗淨，加清水10杯及❶
料，放入電鍋內鍋，外鍋加
水5杯，蒸至開關跳起時取出
放涼。

②將豬肚切條，香菇、紅棗分
別浸水泡軟（圖❶），筍切
條。

③將所有材料放入電鍋內鍋，
加❷料（圖❷），外鍋加水3
杯，蒸至開關跳起時取出。

INGREDIENTS/

1 pork tripe, 1 bamboo shoot, 10
dried black mushrooms, 1¹/₂ oz.
dried red dates

❶ 1 T. cooking wine, 1 stalk green
onion, 2 slices ginger

❷ 6 c. soup stock, 1 T. cooking
wine, 1 t. salt

METHOD/

① Wash pork tripe, place in inner
pan. Add 10 c. water and ❶. Add
5 c. water in rice cooker, steam
until switch turns off. Remove.
Cool.

② Cut pork tripe into thick strips.
Soak dried black mushrooms and
dried red dates in water separately (fig. ❶). Cut bamboo shoot
into thick strips.

③ Place tripe, black mushrooms,
red dates, bamboo shoot and ❷
in inner pan (fig. ❷). Add 3 c.
water in rice cooker, steam until
switch turns off. Remove and
serve.

重點提示／REMARKS

* 豬肚的清洗方法，可參考酸菜肚片湯。
* 先蒸熟的整個豬肚，可在取出後立刻用冷水沖涼，如此可使豬肚的口感變脆。
* 煮豬肚的湯沒有鮮味，故以高湯代替較原湯理想，沒有高湯時要用豬肚湯也可以，
  但較混濁。

* Prepare pork tripe as instructed in "Pickled Mustard and Pork Tripe Soup."
* Cool steamed pork tripe under cold running water. This will make the texture crunchy.
* If soup stock is not available, use the liquid from steaming pork tripe. But the soup will
  not be clear and have some odor.

重點提示／REMARKS

* 百合除新鮮品外亦有乾百合，新鮮百合易熟快爛，洗淨放入略煮即可，但乾百合不易爛。除要先泡水半小時外，可與紅豆同時煮較易爛。
* 紅豆未煮爛前不可放糖調味，否則紅豆煮不爛。
* 電鍋蒸的紅豆湯較清稀，可在蒸好後移至瓦斯爐上再煮滾一下，即可使湯汁變濃稠，但烹調時間較直接火煮省時得多。
* If using dried lily root, soak in water for 30 minutes. Steam with red beans in step ①. * Do not add sugar until red beans become tender.
* After the red bean soup is done, place inner pan on stove. Bring to boil. This will give your a thick red bean soup in a short time.

---

* 買現成的河粉在修出包裹腸粉的部位後，剩餘部分可用來炒或煮湯。
* 除蝦仁外，餡料還可用牛肉或叉燒，以同法製作享受不同口味。 * 亦可撒少許炒香的白芝麻在面上增加香味。
* Save chow fun trimmings for soup or stir-fried dish.
* Substitute beef or Chinese BBQ pork for shrimps, if desired. * Garnish with white sesame seeds on top.

百合紅豆湯 Lily Root and Red Bean Soup

材料／
小紅豆½斤、新鮮百合1球
❶料：白砂糖1杯
作法／
①小紅豆洗淨，加清水12杯，先泡水1小時（圖❶），再放入電鍋，外
　鍋加水5杯，蒸至開關跳起時打開。
②放入洗淨的百合及❶料，外鍋再加水1杯，蒸至開關跳起時，取出
　拌勻即可食用（圖❷）。

INGREDIENTS/
3/4 pound red beans, 1 head fresh lily root, separated into cloves and washed
❶ 1 c. sugar
METHOD/
① Wash red beans, soak in 12 c. water for 1 hour (fig. ❶). Place in rice cooker.
　Add 5 c. water in rice cooker, steam until switch turns off.
② Add separated and washed lily roots and ❶. Add 1 c. water in rice cooker,
　steam until switch turns off. Remove. Stir to blend (fig. ❷). Ready to serve.

蝦仁腸粉 Shrimp in Chow Fun Blanket

材料／
蝦仁6兩、河粉3張、葱1支、香菜1棵
❶料：蛋白½個、鹽¼茶匙、胡椒粉少許、太白粉1茶匙
❷料：蠔油5大匙、糖1大匙、胡椒粉少許、高湯1杯、太白粉水1大
　　匙、麻油少許
作法／
①蝦仁抽淨泥腸後洗淨，拭乾水分，拌入❶料略醃。
②河粉裁成20公分長10公分寬之長段，每張河粉攤開，鋪下蝦仁少
　許（圖❶）。
③將放有蝦仁之河粉捲成寬條狀，並在面上斜劃三刀口（圖❷），放
　在抹過少許油之蒸盤內，放入電鍋，外鍋加水½杯，蒸至開關跳
　·起時取出。
④將❷料另用炒鍋煮開，炒成黏稠狀之調味料盛出，另將蒸好的腸
　粉放盤內，淋上少許調味料後，再撒少許葱花或香菜屑即可食用。

INGREDIENTS/
1/2 pound shelled shrimps, 3 sheets chow fun (rice sheets), 1 stalk green
onion, 1 stalk Chinese parsley
❶ 1/2 egg white, 1/4 t. salt, pinch white pepper, 1 t. cornstarch
❷ 5 T. oyster-flavored sauce, 1 T. sugar, pinch white pepper, 1 c. soup
　stock, 1 T. cornstarch solution, dash sesame oil
METHOD/
① Devein shrimps, rinse. Pat dry. Marinate with ❶.
② Cut chow fun into 8 x 4" rectangles. Place some shrimps on each (fig. ❶).
③ Roll up. Make 3 diagonal slashes on top (fig. ❷). Place on oiled plate. Place
　in rice cooker. Add 1/2 c. water in rice cooker, steam until switch turns off.
　Remove.
④ Heat wok with ❷, bring to boil. Stir-fry until thickened. Remove. Transfer rolls
　on serving platter. Drizzle sauce over. Sprinkle with chopped green onion
　and chopped Chinese parsley.

Pastries and Desserts

99

點心類

＊蝦仁不要碾成泥，最好剁細，如此保有顆粒狀，可使口感較脆。

＊餛飩皮最好買小張而且是薄皮者爲佳，太厚太大均不宜，能買到燒賣專用的皮更好，彈性更足，色澤亦更討喜，但除非專業大量批發，否則一般家庭
　以小張餛飩皮代替即可。

＊Do not smash shrimps. Chop shrimps finely to have a better texture.　＊Use won ton wrappers which are samll and thin, if there is a choice.

＊年糕本身已有極高之甜味，故除花生粉外，不可再加糖，以免太膩。

＊除花生粉外，亦可沾裹椰子粉或芝麻粉。　＊爲避免年糕黏盤，除了盤內先抹油外，亦可在排入每塊年糕前，先用少許油在外皮上抹一下再蒸。

＊Sweet rice cake is sweet enough, do not add sugar.　＊Substitute shredded coconuts or sesame seed powder for peanut powder, if desired.

＊In step ①, grease sliced rice cake before placing on oiled plate to prevent them from sticking.

蝦仁燒賣 Shrimp Shao Mai

材料／

蝦仁½斤、絞肉4兩、香菇4朵、筍2支、餛飩皮4兩

❶料：酒1大匙、鹽½茶匙、醬油½大匙、胡椒粉少許、太白粉水1
大匙

作法／

①蝦仁抽除泥腸，洗淨拭乾，用刀剁碎。

②絞肉再剁細，加入蝦仁及泡軟切碎的香菇、煮熟切碎的筍，全部
混合，並加❶料調味拌勻。

③餛飩皮切除四角（圖❶），每張包入餡料少許，捏成燒賣狀（圖
❷），放入抹過少許油的蒸盤上，放入電鍋，外鍋加水1杯，蒸至開
關跳起時取出即成。

INGREDIENTS/

3/4 pound shelled shrimps, 6 oz. ground pork, 4 dried black mushrooms, 2
bamboo shoots, 6 oz. won ton wrappers

❶ 1 T. cooking wine, 1/2 t. salt, 1/2 T. soy sauce, pinch white pepper, 1 T.
cornstarch solution

METHOD/

① Devein shrimps, rinse. Pat dry. Mince.

② Mince ground pork. Soak dried black mushrooms in water to soften.
Remove stems, mince. Cook bamboo shoot in water until done, mince. Mix
pork, black mushrooms, bamboo shoot, and ❶. Mix well.

③ Trim off cornors of won ton wrapper (fig. ❶). Put some filling in center of
wrapper. Gather sides around filling (fig. ❷). Place on oiled plate. Place in
rice cooker. Add 1 c. water in rice cooker, steam until switch turns off.
Remove and serve.

金沙年糕 Rice Cake with Peanut Powder

材料／

甜年糕½斤

❶料：花生粉4兩

作法／

①年糕切厚粗長片（圖❶），放在抹過少許油的蒸盤上，移入電鍋，
外鍋加水1杯，蒸至開關跳起時取出。

②將蒸軟的年糕挾出，放在花生粉內沾裹一層（圖❷），然後排入盤
內即可食用。

INGREDIENTS/

3/4 pound sweet rice cake

❶ 6 oz. peatnut powder

METHOD/

① Cut rice cake into thick slices (fig. ❶). Place on oiled plate. Place in rice
cooker. Add 1 c. water in rice cooker, steam until switch turns off. Remove.

② Dip rice cake slices in peanut powder to coat (fig. ❷). Arrange on serving
platter and serve.

南瓜糕 Pumpkin Rice Cake

材料／

小型南瓜1個（約2斤重）、糯米粉1斤、絞肉½斤、蘿蔔乾2兩、紅葱酥½杯、香菇3朵

❶料：酒1大匙、醬油1大匙、鹽½茶匙、太白粉水1大匙

❷料：糖2大匙

作法／

①南瓜去皮、籽，切塊，放入電鍋，外鍋加水2杯，蒸至開關跳起時取出，趁熱碾成泥狀。

②蘿蔔乾洗淨、切碎，香菇泡軟、去蒂切碎，用3大匙油先炒紅葱酥，再放入蘿蔔乾及香菇丁同炒，最後加絞肉炒勻，並加❶料調味後，拌勻作成餡料，盛出放涼備用。

③將南瓜泥與糯米粉混合，揉勻成粉糰，並加❷料調味，揉至光滑時，放置片刻備用（圖❶）。

④將粉糰搓長條，再分小粒，每粒按扁，包入餡料少許，用拇指和食指間虎口捏攏，搓圓（圖❷）。

⑤每粒南瓜糕用刀背刻出紋路，並綴上一小根葡萄乾切細做成的蒂頭（圖❸），放在抹過少許油之蒸盤上，放入電鍋，外鍋加水2杯，蒸至開關跳起時即可取出食用。

INGREDIENTS/

1 small pumpkin (about $2^2/_3$ pounds), 3 oz. dried Chinese radish, 3 dried black mushrooms, 1/2 c. fried chopped shallot, 2/3 pound ground pork, $1^1/_3$ pounds sweet rice flour

❶ 1 T. cooking wine, 1 T. soy sauce, 1/2 t. salt, 1 T. cornstarch solution

❷ 2 T. sugar

METHOD/

① Pare pumpkin, remove seeds, cut into pieces. Place in inner pan. Add 2 c. water in rice cooker, steam until switch turns off. Remove. Mash hot pumpkin.

② Rinse dried Chinese radish, mince. Soak dried black mushrooms in water to soften. Remove stems, mince. Heat wok

with 3 T. oil, stir-fry fried chopped shallot, add minced radish and black mushroom, stir well. Add ground pork, stir well. Stir in ❶. Remove, cool.

③ Mix mashed pumpkin, sweet rice flour, and ❷. Knead until smooth. Let stand for a little while (fig. ❶).

④ Shape dough into long rope, cut into small pieces. Flatten with plam. Place some filling in center. Gather edges to enclose filling. Pinch to seal. Roll into small ball (fig. ❷).

⑤ Use blunt edge of knife to make creases. Cut raisin into thin strips to make stems (fig. ❸). Place cakes on oiled plate. Place in rice cooker. Add 1¹/₂ c. water in rice cooker, steam until switch turns off. Remove and serve.

重點提示／REMARKS

* 蒸南瓜糕時，中途要不時將鍋蓋掀開一下，散發部分熱氣，以免蒸氣溫度過高，會使南瓜糕塌陷，影響造型。
* 爲避免蒸好的南瓜糕黏手，不妨蒸前先抹少許油在表皮上即可避免。

* In step ⑤, uncover occasionally during steaming to keep temperature from too high. Otherwise, pumkin rice cakes will collapse.
* Grease the rice cake surface before placing in rice cooker to avoid sticking.

* 購買芋頭時,以重量輕者,質地較乾鬆。
* 本作法之芋頭糕較能保持芋頭絲之形狀,亦可先將芋頭絲加水煮半熟再加入調稀的在來米粉拌勻,然後蒸熟。
* 用電鍋蒸時,可用內鍋的蒸盤爲容器,或盛在飯盒內或鋁箔紙質料的模型,總之粉漿不可太厚,以免不熟。
* 放入電鍋蒸時,一定要在外鍋有水的地方放上鐵架架高食物再蒸,避免水溢入容器內。

* Look for firm taro root that is light for its size.
* For a different texture, you may par-boil shredded taro root, then stir in long-grain rice flour solution, mix well. Place in rice cooker, steam until done.
* Use inner plate, lunch box, or aluminum pan as steaming container. * Place container on rack in rice cooker.

* 若用新鮮蓮子時,不需浸泡,洗淨即可,蒸的時間也不需太久,外鍋改用2杯水即可。 * 在蓮子未蒸爛前不可加糖調味,以免蓮子不爛。
* 桂圓肉若太早放入,會使湯汁變暗,且蒸過久使桂圓肉完全漲開時反而不好吃,本身亦無味。

* If using fresh lotus seeds, do not soak in water. Add 2 c. water in rice cooker instead of 4 c. * Do not add sugar until lotus seeds are tender.
* If adding longans too early, the color of the soup will be darkened and longans will lose flavor.

芋頭糕 Taro Root Cake

材料／
芋頭1個（約1斤4兩）、在來米粉3杯
❶料：鹽2茶匙、清水7杯、胡椒粉少許
❷料：蒜末2大匙、醬油5大匙、糖1大匙、麻油少許

作法／
①芋頭去皮，用刨絲器刨成絲（圖❶）。
②將在來米粉放在大碗內，加水7杯調勻（圖❷），並加入鹽、胡椒粉調味後，先放入炒鍋內，並倒入芋頭絲同炒至黏糊狀時盛入長形模器內，並蓋上保鮮膜。
③放入電鍋，外鍋加水5杯，蒸至開關跳起時取出，放涼。
④食用時可切片煎，亦可切成四方塊回鍋蒸軟後挾食，並將❷料調勻作成沾料。

INGREDIENTS/
1 taro root (about $1^2/_3$ pounds), 3 c. long-grain rice flour
❶ 2 t. salt, 7 c. water, pinch white pepper
❷ 2 T. minced garlic, 5 T. soy sauce, 1 T. sugar, dash sesame oil

METHOD/
① Pare taro root, shred with grater (fig. ❶).
② Place rice flour in mixing bowl, add ❶ (fig. ❷). Mix well. Heat wok, add rice flour mixture and shredded taro root. Stir-fry until thickened. Pour mixture into a rectangular pan, cover with plastic wrap.
③ Place in rice cooker. Add 5 c. water in rice cooker, steam until switch turns off. Remove, cool.
④ Slice and fry before serving. Or cut into squares, reheat in rice cooker. Mix ❷ well. Serve with taro root cake.

三元湯 Three Fruits Soup

材料／
蓮子4兩、紅棗1兩、桂圓肉½兩
❶料：白糖2杯

作法／
①蓮子洗淨，泡水1小時（圖❶）。
②紅棗洗淨，另外用清水浸泡20分鐘，然後將蓮子一同放入電鍋內鍋，加清水8杯（圖❷），外鍋加水4杯，蒸至開關跳起時，再將桂圓肉及❶料放入，外鍋另加水½杯，再蒸5分鐘。
③開關跳起時即可盛出食用，冰涼後風味更佳。

INGREDIENTS/
6 oz. dried lotus seeds, $1^1/_2$ oz. dried red dates, 3/4 oz. pitted dried longans
❶ 2 c. sugar

METHOD/
① Rinse lotus seeds, soak in water for 1 hour (fig. ❶).
② Rinse red dates, soak in water for 20 minutes. Drain lotus seeds and red dates, place in inner pan, cover with 8 c. water (fig. ❷). Add 4 c. water in rice cooker, steam until switch turns off. Add longans and ❶. Add 1/2 c. water in rice cooker, steam for 5 minutes more.
③ Remove and serve. Taste better if serving cold.

Pastries and Desserts

點心類

重點提示／REMARKS

* 煮飯時，開關跳起後，立刻掀蓋，用飯杓將飯粒上下翻動一下，再加蓋燜10分鐘，如此可使米粒軟度均勻。
* 拌入醋與糖後，不可為使米飯轉涼而用飯杓過度攪動米飯，以免米粒碎爛。
* 煎蛋皮時油不可太多，以免蛋液攤不開，加少許太白粉水可使厚度增加並有彈性，亦可用醃漬的黃蘿蔔代替。
* 海苔要用時再打開，萬一用不完下次而變軟時，可放在火上烘乾再用。

* In step ①, uncover as soon as switch turns off. Stir rice with rice paddle. Cover, let stand for 10 minutes. This will make rice have even doneness.
* Do not overstir rice for cooling faster.
* Substitute pickled yellow radish for egg pancake.
* If dried seaweed sheets are dampened by moisture, toast them by waving over high flame for a few seconds.

* 做這道飯所使用的雞腿，以半土雞的肉質較適合。
* 雞湯加入白米中煮飯時，不可太滾燙，稍涼再加入，湯汁可使用蒸雞腿時泌出之湯汁，不夠的話可酌加冷水補足。
* 沾料一定要用燒熱的沙拉油沖入，才可使葱、薑產生香味。

* In step ②, cool chicken broth slightly before adding to rice. If reserved chicken broth is less than 2 cups, add enough water to make 2 cups.
* In step ③, mix seasonings with hot oil to bring out flavor.

壽司 Sushi

料材／
壽司米2杯、洋火腿1塊、蛋1個、肉鬆1杯、海苔1包
❶料：水果醋4大匙、白糖2大匙

作法／
①壽司米洗淨，加水1¾杯浸泡20分鐘後，入鍋煮成飯，趁熱加入❶料拌勻放涼（圖❶）。
②將蛋打散後，加少許鹽及太白粉水拌勻，鍋中熱油1大匙，倒入蛋液煎成蛋皮，取出後切成細長條，洋火腿切長條，肉鬆倒出1杯備用。
③用一只竹簾捲攤開，先鋪1張海苔，再放一層白飯，然後將洋火腿、蛋皮及肉鬆各放少許，捲緊成筒狀（圖❷）。
④用刀沾少許沙拉油後，將捲好的壽司切小段，即可食用。

INGREDIENTS/
2 c. short-grain rice, 4 long strips cooked ham, 1 egg, 1 c. fried shredded pork, 5 sheets dried seaweed (nori seaweed)
❶ 4 T. cider vinegar, 2 T. sugar

METHOD/
① Rinse rice, drain. Soak in 1³/₄ c. water for 20 minutes. Place in rice cooker, steam until done. Stir ❶ in hot rice, mix to blend (fig. ❶). Cool.
② Beat egg slightly, add pinch salt and cornstarch solution, mix well. Heat wok with 1 T. oil. Pour in egg mixture. Rotate wok slowly to spread egg evenly into a thin pancake. Remove. Cut into long strips.
③ Lay 1 sheet seaweed on bamboo rolling mat. Place rice on top. Place some ham, egg and fried shredded pork in line along center of rice. Roll up bamboo mat to form firm roll (fig. ❷).
④ Oil cleaver slightly, cut sushi into small sections. Ready to serve.

海南雞飯 Chicken-Flavored Rice

材料／
白米1杯、雞腿1隻
❶料：葱1支、薑2片、酒1大匙、清水2杯
❷料：雞湯2杯、鹽½茶匙、蒜末1大匙
❸料：葱屑½大匙、薑末½大匙、鹽½茶匙

作法／
①白米洗淨，泡水20分鐘，雞腿洗淨，先氽燙過血水，再加❶料蒸，外鍋加水2杯，蒸至開關跳起時取出，雞腿放涼備用（圖❶）。
②用2大匙油炒香❷料之蒜末後盛出，白米瀝乾水分放電鍋內，加入其他❷料及炒香之蒜末拌勻後煮成飯（圖❷）。
③雞腿切塊排入盤內，蒸好的雞飯盛出，另外將❸料拌勻，淋入2大匙熱油後作成雞腿之沾料即可。

INGREDIENTS/
1 c. short-grain rice, 1 chicken leg
❶ 1 stalk green onion, 2 slices ginger, 1 T. cooking wine, 2 c. water
❷ 2 c. chicken broth, 1/2 t. salt, 1 T. minced garlic
❸ 1/2 T. minced green onion, 1/2 T. minced ginger, 1/2 t. salt

METHOD/
① Rinse rice, soak in water for 20 minutes. Rinse chicken leg, blanch in boiling water to remove scum. Place in inner pan, add ❶. Add 2 c. water in rice cooker, steam until switch turns off. Remove. Cool chicken (fig. ❶). Reserve chicken broth.
② Heat wok with 2 T. oil, stir-fry minced garlic until fragrant. Drain rice, place in inner pan. Add 2 c. chicken broth, salt and stir-fried garlic. Mix to blend. Place in rice cooker, steam until done (fig. ❷). Remove.
③ Chop chicken into pieces, place on plate. Transfer rice to plate. Mix ❸, add 2 T. hot oil. Serve with chicken.

八寶飯 Eight Treasures Rice Pudding

材料/
圓糯米1½杯、豆沙4兩、青紅
絲各1包、甜納豆1兩、葡萄乾
3大匙
❶料：豬油2大匙、白糖2大匙
作法/
①圓糯米洗淨,加水2杯浸泡10
　分鐘後,放入電鍋煮成糯米
　飯,取出後趁熱加入❶料拌
　勻(圖❶)。
②取一個大碗,先在碗內抹1大
　匙豬油,再將青紅絲及甜納
　豆、葡萄乾排成整齊之圖案
　(圖❷)。
③先放一半糯米飯在圖案上,
　輕輕抹平,然後填入壓平之
　豆沙為餡,再將剩下的糯米
　飯鋪在上面抹平,放入電鍋
　再蒸,外鍋加水1杯,蒸至開
　關跳起時取出,扣在盤內即
　成。

INGREDIENTS/
1¹/₂ c. short-grain sweet rice, 6 oz.
red bean paste, 5g. shredded red
candied fruit, 5g. shredded green
candied fruit, 1¹/₂ oz. candied
kidney beans, 3 T. raisins
❶ 2 T. lard, 2 T. sugar

METHOD/
① Rinse rice, soak in 2 c. water for
　10 minutes. Place in rice cooker,
　steam until done. Remove. Add
　❶ to hot rice. Mix well (fig. ❶).
② Grease medium bowl with 1 T.
　lard. Arrange shredded red and
　green candies fruits, candied
　kidney beans and raisins in
　circles around bottom and up to
　edge of bowl (fig. ❷).
③ Spread 1/2 rice mixture over fruits
　carefully. Smooth surface. Place
　a layer red bean paste over rice.
　Cover with remaining rice.
　Smooth surface. Place in rice
　cooker. Add 1 c. water in rice
　cooker, steam until switch turns
　off. Remove. Invert bowl on
　severing platter, remove bowl.

重點提示

＊甜口味的食品,要使用圓糯米,較有黏性,不宜用長糯米。
＊蒸八寶飯時,喜歡口感軟爛者,直接放入蒸即可,不喜過軟者,要在飯面上加蓋
　一層保潔膜再蒸,因為電鍋會滴水。
＊排圖案前,大碗先抹少許豬油,並放入冰箱冰過再排,可因豬油之凝固,幫助圖
　案之配料固定而不致滑落。

REMARKS

* Use short-grain sweet rice for desserts and long-grain sweet rice savory dishes.
* The "eight treasures" can be varied according to your taste.
* If you don't want the steamed sweet rice to be too soft, cover rice with plastic wrap before placing in rice cooker in step ③.
* Grease bowl with lard, cool in refrigerator. This will make "eight treasures" stick well.

草莓布丁 Strawberry Custard

材料／
蛋2個、鮮奶1杯、玉米粉水2大匙
❶料：草莓果醬4大匙、糖2大匙、清水1杯、太白粉水1大匙
作法／
①蛋打散，加入鮮奶及玉米粉水拌勻（圖❶）。
②用一只細網將打勻的蛋液過濾一下，盛入平底蒸碗內（圖❷），放入電鍋蒸，外鍋加水2杯，蒸至開關跳起時取出，放涼。
③將❶料放入炒鍋煮開，炒勻成糊狀調味料，再將放涼的布丁扣出，淋在面上即成。

INGREDIENTS/
2 eggs, 1 c. milk, 2 T. cornstarch solution
❶ 4 T. strawberry jam, 2 T. sugar, 1 c. water, 1 T. cornstarch solution
METHOD/
① Whisk eggs. Add milk and cornstarch solution, mix well (fig. ❶).
② Strain egg mixture into casserole (fig. ❷). Place in rice cooker. Add 2 c. water in rice cooker, steam until switch turns off. Remove. Cool.
③ Heat wok with ❶. Bring to boil. Stir until thickened. Invert cooled custard on serving platter. Unmold. Drizzle sauce over custard and serve.

桂花涼糕 Cassia Blossom Rice Cake

材料／
圓糯米2杯、豆沙6兩、耐熱塑膠紙袋4張
❶料：桂花醬3大匙
作法／
①圓糯米洗淨，加水2杯，浸泡20分鐘後煮成糯米飯，取出後趁熱攪碎（圖❶）。
②將耐熱塑膠袋拆開成一大張，先鋪少許糯米飯，再將豆沙搓長條放在米飯中間（圖❷）。
③將塑膠袋捲起，使糯米飯將豆沙包在中間，搓成長條狀捲緊，放入冰箱冰涼。
④冰涼後切小段排入盤內，食用時將紙撕開，面上澆少許桂花醬即成。

INGREDIENTS/
2 c. short-grain sweet rice, 1/2 pound red bean paste
❶ 3 T. preserved cassia blossom (kwei-hwa)
METHOD/
① Rinse short-grain sweet rice. Soak in 2 c. water for 30 minutes. Place in rice cooker, steam until done. Remove. Mash hot rice (fig. ❶).
② Place 1/4 rice on 12" x 12" plastic wrap. Shape 1/4 red bean paste into rope, place in center of rice (fig. ❷).
③ Roll up plastic wrap, press firmly to shape it. Refrigerate until cooled.
④ Cut cooled cake into small sections, arrange on serving platter. Remove plastic wrap before serving. Drizzle with preserved cassia blossom.

國立中央圖書館出版品預行編目資料

電鍋菜 = Rice-cooker cookbook / 梁瓊白著；
田世璞譯. -- 初版. -- 臺北市：躍昇文化出
版 ；[臺北縣]中和市：三友總經銷，民84
　面 ；　公分. -- (品味誌 ；16)
ISBN 957-630-334-6(平裝)

1. 食譜 - 中國

427.11　　　　　　　　　　　　　　84000020

●品味誌16●　　　　　　　　　　　　　ISBN 957-630-334-6 (平裝)

電鍋菜
RICE-COOKER COOKBOOK

作　　　者／梁瓊白　　　　　道具提供／義富股份有限公司
譯　　　者／田世璞　　　　　圖片攝影／上顏廣告攝影有限公司
發 行 人／吳貴仁
執行編輯／林伶美
編　　審／曾美珠
美術編輯／邱元昌
出 版 者／躍昇文化事業有限公司
　　　　　CULTURE & LIFE PUBLISHING COMPANY
社　　　址／台北市仁愛路四段122巷63號9樓
　　　　　9F. 63. Lane 122 Sec. 4 Jen-Ai Rd. Taipei, Taiwan, R.O.C.
電　　　話／(02)7031828　7057118　　傳眞電話／(02)7024333
劃撥帳號／1188888-8　　劃撥帳戶／躍昇文化事業有限公司
登 記 證／局版台業字第3994號
印　　　刷／皇甫彩藝印刷有限公司
電　　　話／(02)3035871　　傳眞電話／(02)3076874
台北總經銷／學英文化事業有限公司
地　　　址／新店市中正路四維巷2弄5號5樓
電　　　話／(02)2187307　　傳眞電話／(02)2187021
新加坡總代理／諾文文化事業私人有限公司　Novum Organum Publishing House Pte. Ltd.
地　　　址／2 kallang Pudding Road#07-15 Mactech Industrial Building, SPORE 1334
電　　　話／8420278
初　　　版／1995年1月
初版十一刷／1996年2月　　　　　　　　　定價／新台幣300元